Miracle Plays

Seven Medieval Plays for Modern Players

Seven Medieval Plays for Modern Players

Miracle Plays

adapted by ANNE MALCOLMSON

Illustrated by Pauline Baynes

HOUGHTON MIFFLIN COMPANY BOSTON

The Riverside Press Cambridge

DEDICATION

SOME YEARS ago my neighbor Kit, who was going on twelve, asked me to find a play that he and his friends might give. At least eight speaking parts were required. Provision should be made also for a few animals, to accommodate talented little sisters and brothers who could moo like cows and roar like lions. It wasn't easy to find a vehicle that met our several standards, until I recalled *The Chester Deluge*, a miracle play about Noah's Ark, which I had read in college. *This* filled the bill. The only available copy, unfortunately, was printed in Early Modern English, a little steep for Kit and his players. So, since fools rush in where angels fear to tread, I "translated" it.

That was the start of this collection. There were other miracle plays and other persons, going on twelve and older, who might enjoy them if the language barrier were broken ever so little.

Now, to Kit and George and Toby and the others, I acknowledge my debt and send my affectionate greetings. To my husband, Earl von Storch, I dedicate this book of *Miracle Plays*.

ANNE MALCOLMSON VON STORCH

CONTENTS

Introduction

As you can see from the title, this is a book about miracles. Most of you know what a miracle is — something wonderful and strange that happens even when you are certain that it can't happen. If a pear tree, frozen and bare, were to put out leaves and blossoms in the middle of winter, that would be a miracle. If the sickle of the new moon were to slice off the top of a mountain, that would be a miracle. Many of you are familiar with the miracles that are recounted in the Bible.

The stories of the plays that are presented here are all about miracles, in this last sense of the word. Each one tells the story of a wonderful and miraculous event. Noah and his family are saved from a flood which destroys the whole world. The statue of St. Nicholas catches a band of robbers and punishes them for their crime. In *The Nativity*, *The Shepherds' Play* and *Herod and the Magi*, we have the story of that most wonderful miracle of all, the Birth of Christ.

These plays, however, are miracle plays, as well as plays about miracles. And what, you ask, are miracle plays? Some of you may already have read a good deal about the Middle Ages — the days of the Crusades, of knights and of chivalry, of feudal lords, and of the building of the Gothic cathedrals. We might say that the Middle Ages were roughly the centuries between the fall of the old Roman Empire and the discovery of the New World by Columbus. For our present purposes, we can narrow the time a little, from the time of William the Conqueror until shortly after Joan of Arc.

The ordinary people of the day had very little in the way of entertainment. Serfs and free farmers worked hard on their lands, from sunup to sundown, tending their sheep and cattle and producing their crops. In towns and cities, the craftsmen — weavers, plasterers, leatherworkers, harness makers, carpenters, together with the common laborers — worked equally hard. Great lords had their minstrels, their jousts and tournaments, to keep them amused. But there were few shows for the common folk.

The people of the Middle Ages were very religious. Most of their life, not spent in everyday chores, was centered in their churches. The church ceremonies, the singing of the masses and the celebration of the rituals, took place in Latin, which few of the congregation could understand. Even so, these ceremonies were splendid to watch and to hear, and many of the worshipers knew the basic meaning behind the Latin words.

Just when the practice began, no one surely knows, but occasionally the priests and choir boys would act out parts of the ceremony. At Eastertide, for instance, three priests representing the three Maries would approach a spot in the apse of the church that served as the tomb of Christ. Another priest representing an angel sang to them *"Quem quaeritis?"* — which is Latin for "Whom do ye seek?" The three Maries replied in Latin that they sought Jesus of Nazareth. Then the angel told them, "He is risen!"

These questions and answers make up what is really a very simple little play, in which the priests acted out parts, even though it was included as a part of the church ceremony. Gradually other portions of the Bible story were acted out in a similar fashion. Before long, fairly complicated plays were evolved.

As time went on, subjects not in the Bible and not connected with the proper church services, were acted out, too. The lives of the saints were often presented in this fashion. St. Nicholas, who had a great many dramatic adventures in his career, was one of the most popular subjects.

Sooner or later, these religious plays had to move outside the church. Then they were presented out of doors on the appropriate days of church festivals. The saints' adventures were given on saints' days. At Christmastime there were several shows — the Shepherds and the Manger Scene on Christmas Eve, the Adoration of the Three Kings, or Herod and the Massacre of the Innocents, on Twelfth Night. Christ's Crucifixion and Resurrection were acted out at Easter. Stories from the Old Testament were gradually introduced. The Creation of the World, Adam and Eve, Noah's Ark, Abraham and Isaac — all were made into playlets. These had two effects. They helped the people to learn the stories of the Bible, on the one hand. On the other hand, they provided the townsfolk a good deal of fun and excitement, for who does not like to go to the theater?

By the time with which we are primarily concerned, several of the cities had built up large repertories of these little plays. Why, when, and how it happened, we do not know for sure. Eventually, the craftsmen of the cities took over the job of producing and acting out the Bible stories. Sometimes, frequently at Whitsuntide, after the Feast of the Ascension in the spring, everyone in town took three or four days off to celebrate the religious festival. One of its brightest features was the presentation of the pageants, beginning with the Creation of the World and ending with the Last Judgment. In some towns there were as many as forty plays presented. Often the whole production took three whole days, from early dawn until the failing of the afternoon light. Since all of these little playlets had to do with the subject of a miracle, they were given the name of "miracle plays."

The craftsmen of those days, in order to protect themselves in their businesses, joined together in guilds. These guilds were associations or clubs, if you will, that made the rules for all the men who worked at any one trade. The weavers of a town organized a Weavers' Guild, which set the prices for cloth and established the standards for training new weavers, among other things. The armorers, the bakers, the dyers, the fletchers (who made bows and arrows), all had their own organizations. Each of these organizations was assigned a particular "miracle" to perform in the town series of plays, preferably one which was suitable to its trade. The goldsmiths, who could display their fine skills in the crowns and rich presents which were brought to the Christ Child, usually produced the play of the Three Kings. The armorers, who had plenty of weapons on hand for properties, acted out the plays that called for soldiers. The play of *Noah's Flood,* which appears in this book, was given by the waterleaders and drawers of Chester. The dyers of Wakefield produced the episode of Pharaoh's driving the Children of Israel into the Red Sea, presumably because they could dye the Red Sea red.

The craftsmen themselves, masters, journeymen, and apprentices, acted out all the parts, including those of the women. Instead of being paid for their services, they were more likely to be fined for not doing the job well — for being late to rehearsals and performances, for not learning their lines, and even for acting poorly.

The stage on which the productions were given seems surprising to us. This was the floor of a cart or a wagon. These carts were called "pageants," and from these our modern word "pageant" has come to mean a great show or spectacle. The reason for using carts is clear when you understand what happened. Even though the cities were small by our standards, their public squares were still not large enough to hold all the citizens and visitors who wanted to see the shows. Consequently, the plays were given in a sort of procession that moved from square to square around the town, each episode being presented several times so that everyone could see it. Furthermore, there was no way of shifting scenery quickly in any one square.

The Creation "pageant," or wagon, would move into its first station, perhaps in front of the church, at early sunrise. The actors would jump down, tie up their horses, set the stage in order in the wink of an eye, and proceed with their play. Once they were finished, they would pack up and move on to their next station, maybe the town marketplace. Then the second "pageant," bringing possibly the story of Cain and Abel, would move onto the church plaza. In this way, every episode carried its own scenery with it, and everyone who had the patience could stay in one spot to see the whole series. It must have been hard at times for the spectators to decide what to do — whether to stay to see the performance from beginning to end, or to move along with a pageant to see a favorite play over and over again.

The audience, of course, had to stand in the square. Those who were fortunate might find a window or a balcony from which to watch in comfort. No doubt many of the spectators climbed trees or even roofs to watch.

There were still other differences from modern shows. There was no pulling of curtains between episodes to separate the scenes within each playlet. The action took place without interruption. I have taken considerable liberty here by dividing each little drama, where I thought it necessary, into scenes, to make it easier to read, as well as to prepare, in case you should wish to give a performance. You should keep in mind, however, that the guildsmen paid no attention to such divisions. For instance, when Abraham and Isaac left their home to make their sacrifice upon the distant mountain, they probably did not leave the stage. One corner of the front of the "pageant" represented their dwelling place. A raised spot at the center backstage represented the mountain. It was up to the audience to imagine that their brief walk about the platform indicated a trip of considerable distance.

Another difference is that the miracle plays were probably sung. The very earliest church plays were undoubtedly chanted as part of the religious service. All of the selections in this book are given in a type of verse form which suggests a musical setting. Some of them, indeed, are very like the old ballads. I have not tried to include the music, much of which has been lost. Some of the tunes, nevertheless, have come down to us. One of the best known is the "Coventry Carol," that lovely Christmas carol which begins, "Lullay, thou little tiny child," which many of you know. This was originally included in the Coventry episode of "The Slaughter of the Innocents." The song was sung by the grieving women of Bethlehem to their babies, after Herod had ordered the killing of all the boy children in the country.

Even though each "pageant" had its own scenery, this was still very crude. The floor of the cart served as the main stage. Underneath, between the wheels, the actors put the finishing touches on their costumes and jostled each other, trying to get into position for their entrances. Usually a simple curtain or wall was considered enough for the back of the stage. There were few painted backdrops and no spectacular lighting effects, as we know them. If the action called for something special, such as a gateway or a stable, this was indicated according to the taste and resources of the guild. Occasionally fairly elaborate scenes were prepared. The thatchers gave one of the plays of the Birth of Jesus; we can imagine that they built a pleasing manger scene, with a real thatched roof over the stable. One very enterprising stage manager is said to have found the head of a dead whale which had been washed ashore. He cleaned it up and set it in place, with two boys to open and shut the jaws. It made a very dramatic Gateway to Hell. Some of the episodes called for trap doors through which the devils could pop up onto the Earth. Such doors were cut in the floors of the wagons.

One bit of stage construction that appeared in many of the episodes was a sort of superstructure which, for want of a better term, I have called the "High Place." This represented Heaven. A rather rickety framework, or second story, was built over the main stage. It had to be light in weight to be carried about the town. From this upper story, God or His angels spoke to the humans below. A flimsy ladder provided the way for the angel to ascend. The audience must have held its breath now and then, for fear lest he trip on his robes and come crashing down into the world.

Costumes depended on the story to be told and on the wealth and imagination of the craftsmen telling it. We may be sure that most of the ordinary characters wore their own clothes. The shepherds dressed like English shepherds, not like the shepherds of Judaea. Kings and noblemen might be richly dressed. Heathen princes and other infidels, such as Barbarus, were very likely dressed as Turks, with turbans, gorgeous sashes, and long bloomerlike trousers, with little regard for historical accuracy. Herod, for instance, who was actually the governor of a Roman province, brandishes a falchion, a curved sword, typical of the Ottoman soldiers a thousand years after his day. Herod was, however, an enemy of Christendom, and as such he was pictured as a Turk, the most familiar enemy in the time of the Crusades. Devils were got up in tights and grotesque outfits. One devil is described as having lighted torches sticking out of his ears. The "cappers," or hatmakers, of Chester gave the play of "The Prophets," who, no doubt, wore handsome headdresses.

Two of the plays in this book, the St. Nicholas plays, are a little different from the other five in their history. Strangely enough these two, which are the latest in subject matter, are the earliest of all. These two have been translated from the Latin of eleventh century manuscripts found in the north of France. One of these, *The Statue of St. Nicholas,* is known to have been written by an English monk who lived a part of his life on the Continent. He had the delightful name of Hilarius, which fitted his sense of humor very well. We do know that these two plays were performed in the church by monks, not by guildsmen on "pageants." I have included them because there is reason to believe they were given in England, as well as in France.

One aspect of the miracle plays which is sometimes difficult for us to understand is the mixture of fun and religion. Many of these old episodes are very, very funny. The devils are normally comedians. Noah's wife gives her poor henpecked husband a bad time of it. The statue of St. Nicholas is roundly thrashed in good low comedy style for losing the treasure which Barbarus entrusted to it. Strangest of all, to some of us moderns, the Birth of Jesus in *The Shepherds' Play* is preceded by a rollicking piece about sheep-stealing. The fun, however, is not all. Once the fooling is finished, the spirit of the play is reverent.

When you read these plays which follow, you must remember that for several hundred years we have kept our church-going and our entertainment-going separate. To us religion is a serious, if not a solemn, matter. Comedy is something else again. To the people of the Middle Ages, religion was serious, but it was not necessarily solemn. They were not at all disrespectful. Their church services were serious indeed. But they saw nothing wrong in having fun, even when they were presenting Bible stories in front of the church steps.

In this connection I should call your attention to another type of change that I have made from the original versions. There was nothing shocking to a medieval audience in the idea that God might be impersonated by a mortal actor. To many persons today, however, the notion is distasteful. Consequently, wherever possible, as in *Noah's Flood*, I have substituted an angel for the role originally assigned as "God." In other cases, as in *Abraham and Isaac*, where it would be confusing to make such a substitution, I have indicated that God's voice is to be heard from off stage. In the early pageants, the part was played like any other, doubtless by some senior guildsman whose character made him seem worthy of the honor.

Some of you may be interested in knowing a little about the language in which the first five plays were given. If you are not, you may skip this next paragraph or so. You and I speak Modern English; you've no doubt heard of Old English; and some may have heard of Middle English. Our English language has grown and changed with our history. Old English, or Anglo-Saxon, was the language spoken by the people of Beowulf's time, by the Angles and Saxons and Jutes who invaded the British Isles after the Romans left. When the Normans came over under William the Conqueror, they brought with them their own Norman French. For a while the two languages lived side by side. Gradually, however, as the Anglo-Saxons and the Normans intermarried and absorbed each other's customs, their languages "married," too. And so there evolved the earliest form of what we know as English. It is fairly rough sounding to our ears, and it has no firmly fixed rules of spelling. This language, more often spoken than written, has been called Middle English, or Early Modern English. This is the language of the miracle plays. It is not so different a way of speaking from our speech as, say, French or German. It is, however, difficult to read, unless you have studied it.

Just for fun, here is a sample. When the First Shepherd complains of his lot, he says:

"Lord, What these weders ar cold! And I am yll happyd.
I am nere-hand dold, so long haue I nappyd.
My legys thay fold, my fyngers ar chappyd;
It is not as I wold, for I am al lappyd
    In sorow."

You can probably catch the sense of his complaint. The "weders" are our "weathers," or storms, but possibly colder. His fingers are chapped. "Wold" is our "would" or "would like things to be," and "lappyd" means "surrounded." In other words, he's wrapped up in sorrow and miserably uncomfortable. It would be something of a strain for you to have to work out the whole play.

I have tried here to keep a few of the early English words and expressions, so that you can feel a little "medieval" as you read or speak the lines. In some verses it has been easy to let things alone and to bring only the spelling up to date. In others, I've changed things around a bit, so that you can understand the lines without scratching your heads. If you come across an expression that really stumps you, look it up in the glossary, or dictionary, at the back of the book.

The miracle plays aren't hard to find, if you're really interested.

These, and others like them, have been published in their original form in several books for college students and for scholars. But boys and girls can and should enjoy them, too, just as boys and girls like to read the stories of Robin Hood and of King Arthur, which originally were told in even more difficult language. I hope that you will have fun reading these old scripts as they are "translated" in this book; but I hope even more that you may be able to try your hands at giving them. After all, plays are plays, and they are meant to be acted.

Noah's Flood

From the Chester Play of THE DELUGE

CAST *of* CHARACTERS

THE ANGEL	SHEM'S WIFE
NOAH	HAM'S WIFE
SHEM, *Noah's Son*	JAPHETH'S WIFE
HAM, *Noah's Son*	VILLAGE WOMEN, *friends of*
JAPHETH, *Noah's Son*	*Noah's Wife*
NOAH'S WIFE	ANIMALS

Scene I

The stage is set to represent a fairly open space, perhaps a village green. On one side, a little to the back, is the High Place, a balcony or ladder from which the Angel will speak. In the center back of

2

the stage is a space in which the Ark will be built. It may be advisable to have some sort of framework already in place. There are entrances right and left.

The Angel enters and climbs to the High Place. Noah, his Wife, his Sons and their Wives enter the stage. Seeing the Angel, they kneel.

ANGEL

He speaks very solemnly to the audience.

> The Lord, Who all this world hath wrought,
> Heaven and earth, all out of nought,
> Hath seen his people, in deed and thought,
>   Settled sore in sin.
> Mankind that He made He will destroy,
> With snakes and beasts and birds that fly!
> For as they are, they Him annoy,
>   These folk that dwell therein.

He turns and speaks directly to Noah.

> Therefore, Noah, His servant free —
> A righteous man, as He doth see —
> A ship thou now shalt build for thee
>   Of timbers dry and light.
> A ship three hundred cubits long,
> And fifty wide, to make it strong,
> And thirty high. And see that thou
>   Dost measure it aright.
> A galley thou shalt build thereto,
> And cabins lined with bunks below.

He becomes threatening.

> For with a flood the Lord shall slay
>   Mankind that He hath made.

Noah rises from his knees to address the Heavens.

NOAH   Ah, Lord, I thank Thee loud and still
That Thou hast shown me Thy good will,
To spare me and my house as well,
 For Thou art ever kind.
Thy bidding, Lord, I shall fulfill,
And never more Thee grieve nor grill,
For Thou wilt save me from the ill
 That threatens all mankind.

The Angel climbs down from the High Place and leaves the stage.
When he is gone, Noah addresses his family, who rise.

Be quick, you men and women all!
Help me, no matter what befall,
To build this ship, from mast to hull,
 As God hath bade us do!

Noah walks about the stage, sending his family off one by one to
fetch things, giving them orders in pantomime. When they are
gone he inspects the spot on which the Ark will be built. Noah
comes forward as Shem enters, carrying an axe. Shem comes to
the center front of the stage and brandishes his axe at the audience.

SHEM   Father, I am more than ready!
An axe I have, both true and steady,
As sharp as any in all this city,
 The beams to chop and hew.

Shem pretends to use his axe on an imaginary log, then moves off
toward the back as Ham enters, waving a hatchet. Ham comes to
the center front.

HAM   I have a hatchet wondrous keen,
To bite wood well, as will be seen.
A better one, as well I ween,
 There is not in this town!

Ham pretends to use his hatchet, then retires to join Shem as Japheth enters, carrying a hammer and a wooden peg. Japheth comes to the center front.

JAPHETH And I can make a wondrous pin
And with this hammer knock it in!

Japheth pretends to hammer his peg into a board. Shem and Ham come forward as Noah speaks to the three of them.

NOAH Go all of you, without more din,
And work this ship upon.

Noah and his sons begin to put up the framework of the Ark. After they have set it in place, Noah's wife comes in, bent under the weight of a heavy load of wood, planks and beams. She comes to the center front and speaks very sarcastically.

NOAH'S WIFE
And we shall bring the timber, too!

She dumps the wood off her back and kicks it. Then she turns to the audience and simpers.

> There's little else women can do!
> We are too frail to undergo
>> Any great travail.

She glares at Noah and stalks off the stage. Shem's wife enters, pushing a heavy chopping block laboriously to the front center. She stretches and speaks to Noah.

SHEM'S WIFE

> Here is a good chopping block.
> On this thing you may hew and hack!

Aside to the audience

> There'll be none idle in this flock,
>> Whether or not we sail.

Shem's Wife moves off stage, rubbing her back. Ham's Wife enters, carrying two heavy pails. She puts them down beside the chopping block and speaks to the audience.

HAM'S WIFE

> A pair of heavy pails I fetch,
> To caulk the ship with tar and pitch.
> It must be smeared at every stitch,
>> Each board and crack and pin.

Ham's Wife stretches and leaves the stage. Enter Japheth's Wife, pretending to pick up firewood.

JAPHETH'S WIFE

> And I shall gather faggots here,
> To build a fire and prepare
> Your evening dinner, hearty fare,
>> When all of you come in.

Japheth's Wife leaves the stage. The sons begin to work on the Ark. Noah addresses the audience.

NOAH Now, in the Lord's name, I begin
  To build this vessel, which within
  We shall be ready for to win
   The battle of the flood.

The three sons work on the Ark, while Noah bustles around supervising. Shem pretends to be nailing boards to the Ark, but turns to the audience as he speaks.

SHEM These boards I nail here together
  To keep us safe from the weather,
  That we may sail hither and thither
   And stay dry on this wood!

Ham holds up a small tree or a pole, which he shows to the audience.

HAM Of this tree I shall make the mast,
  Tied with cables that will last
  And sailyards, to meet every blast
   Of the unfriendly wind.

Japheth holds up sails and ropes.

JAPHETH With topgallant and jib and main,
With proper rigging, ropes and twine,
We'll sail forth at the coming rain!

When the Ark is finished, Noah looks it over on all sides, then beams with satisfaction and speaks to his sons.

NOAH The ship is good, I find.

He turns and calls to his wife.

Wife!

Noah's Wife appears at the side of the stage. He leads her to the center and proudly shows her the Ark.

In this castle we shall be safe.
Our sons and we herein shall live.

Noah's Wife looks it over, shaking her head and showing her disgust.

NOAH'S WIFE
I have no love for yonder sieve
And all these goings-on!
I will not enter yonder shed!

She starts to leave the stage. Noah tries to look stern.

NOAH Good wife, now do as I thee bid!

She turns and faces him and snaps her fingers in his face.

NOAH'S WIFE
Indeed not! For I see no need,
Though you ask all day long.

Noah turns to the audience in exasperation.

NOAH Oh, Lord! Are women crabbèd aye
And never meek! That I can say.

> This is well proven here today
> In witness of you all.

He walks up to his wife.

> Good wife, forget this silly stand
> That you are making on the land.

He whispers to her.

> They'll think you have the upper hand.

Aside, to himself.

> Which you do, by Saint Paul!

Noah's Wife flounces off the stage. Noah shrugs his shoulders at the audience, then he and his sons follow her.

End of Scene I

Scene II

The Angel enters and climbs to the High Place. Noah enters to survey the Ark. As the Angel calls his name, he stops in the center of the stage and kneels.

ANGEL
> Noah! Bring thou thy company
> Within the ship that here I see,
> For none so righteous man there be
>   In this world living.
> Of beasts of all sorts, thou shalt carry
> Two and two with thee to tarry,
> Male and female that can marry,
>   Their kind preserving!
> Of snakes and birds, two and no more
> Of each, as with the beasts before.
> These too shall enter yonder door

Before He sends the weather.
And all the food that will be eaten
To the hold must now be gotten,
So that no beast may be forgotten.
  And do this altogether.
Seven cocks have yet to crow
While you bring these beasts below.

The Angel pauses and speaks very solemnly.

After this, it shall be so!
  The Lord will man annoy.
Forty days and nights the rain
Will fall, to punish mankind's sin.
For what the Lord doth hate therein,
  He will indeed destroy!

NOAH Lord, to Thy bidding I shall bow.
Thou dost no other Grace allow.
I shall fulfill it here somehow,
  For gracious Thou hast been.
One hundred winters and a score
This ship's been building, for I swore
  To help mankind from sin.

The Angel climbs down from the High Place and leaves the stage.
Noah rises, and leaves from the opposite entrance.

End of Scene II

Scene III

Noah bustles onto the stage carrying supplies which he puts into
the Ark. He stands beside the deck as Shem enters, leading a num-
ber of large animals.

SHEM   Sire, here are lions, leopards, too,
            Horse and mare, and ox and cow,
            Goats and sheep and swine enow
                To stable, as you see.

*Shem leads his animals with some difficulty into the Ark. Ham
enters leading several other large animals.*

HAM   Camels, asses, here you find,
            Buck and doe, hart and hind,
            And beasts of other lesser kind,
                As you have asked of me.

*Ham leads his animals into the Ark. Japheth enters leading several
small, frisking creatures, and carrying a basket of greens.*

JAPHETH Here are little dogs, also,
         Otter, fox and badger, too,
         And rabbits, hopping to and fro,
           With greens for them to eat.

Japheth leads his charges into the Ark. Noah's Wife enters, leading a pack of snarling beasts.

NOAH'S WIFE
         And here are wolves and bears to pet,
         Apes, and owls, and marmoset,
         Weasels, squirrels, and others that
           Are careless whom they bite!

She leads her beasts into the Ark, returns, and leaves the stage. Shem's Wife comes in, leading small animals.

SHEM'S WIFE
         Still more beasties for this house!
         Cats are making their miaows.
         Here a rat, and there a mouse.

Aside to the audience

They'll never live together!

She takes her animals into the Ark. Ham's Wife enters, leading several large birds, and carrying a basket of fish.

HAM'S WIFE

Here are great birds by the score,
Herons and cranes that wade the shore,
Swans and peacocks, with fishes for
To feed them in the weather.

She leads her birds into the Ark. Japheth's Wife enters, carrying many small birds.

JAPHETH'S WIFE

Here are cocks and kites and crows,
Rooks and ravens, many rows,
Cuckoos, curlews, chickadees,
Each pair of its kind.
Here are doves and ducks and drakes,
Redshanks running through the lakes,
And every bird that singing wakes
Among them you can find.

Exit Japheth's Wife into the Ark. Noah's Wife, accompanied by a group of her friends, enters the stage. In pantomime she points out the Ark to them and they all pretend to whisper and laugh at it. Noah steps forward and speaks crossly.

NOAH   Now, Wife, come in! Why stand you there?
        You are too stubborn. That I swear!
        Come in, silly old woman, ere
            It raineth and we drown.

Noah's Wife steps up to him angrily.

NOAH'S WIFE
        Ah, Noah, set thee up thy sail!
        And may thy voyage be full of bale!
        I tell thee, Husband, without fail,
            I will not leave this town.

She gestures toward her friends.

        Unless my friends come too within,
        I'll take no further step. Not one!
        They shall not drown, by good St. John,
            If I can save their life!
        They love me full well, more than thou,
        And thou wilt let them perish, now!
        Be off, old man, and see if thou
            Canst get thee a new wife!

She turns to her friends, who gather around her sympathetically. Noah goes to the door of the Ark and calls inside.

NOAH   Shem!

Shem enters from the doorway.

        Thy mother is mad, I trow.
        Another like her I do not know.

SHEM   Father, I'll fetch her in right now,
            No matter what the tale.

He comes forward and speaks to his mother.

> Mother, my father sends me for thee
> To bring thee in this ship before thee.
> The wind is rising, the sky is swarthy,
> And we are ready to sail.

NOAH'S WIFE

> Son, go to him and say him nay.
> I will not budge from here today.

Noah loses his patience.

NOAH   Wife, enter!

Aside to the audience.

> I shall rue the day.

To his wife, crossly

> Or else drown there without!

Ham appears from the doorway of the Ark.

HAM   Father, shall we all fetch her in?

NOAH   Yea, with the Lord's blessing and mine.
> But hurry! We are wasting time,
> And of her wits I doubt.

Ham followed by Japheth comes down to where Noah's Wife is standing. Shem moves into place, so that he and Ham stand behind her and between her and her friends. Japheth kneels in front of her.

JAPHETH Mother, we pray you all together,
> Your loving children and their father,
> Come into the ship for fear of the weather,
> As the Angel hath us taught.

NOAH'S WIFE

That I will not, though loud you call,
Unless I bring my gossips all.

Shem grabs her, while Ham chases the friends off stage. Japheth meanwhile has risen. As Shem speaks the three boys have her firmly under control, one holding each arm and one close behind, ready to push her.

SHEM   In faith, dear Mother, yet you shall,
Whether you like it or not!

The three boys force her to the door of the Ark. Noah comes up to meet her and holds out his hands.

NOAH   Welcome, Wife, unto this ship!

She stops kicking and speaks furiously.

NOAH'S WIFE

Dear Husband, have this for thy lip!

She slaps his face, and then is bustled into the Ark. Noah rubs his face and groans.

NOAH   Marry, no one hath such a whip!

He looks about him briefly, then sighs.

Ah, it is good to be still!

While Noah is standing beside the Ark, the Angel enters solemnly to the High Place, bearing a pitcher of water. Noah sees him and falls to his knees. The Angel slowly pours the water out of the pitcher, to indicate that the rains are beginning. Then he climbs down from the High Place and leaves the stage. Noah rises to his feet and scans the horizon. He calls out to his children.

Children, I think our ship is moving.
To tarry here doth set me grieving.

Over the land the flood is spreading.
May God now work His will.

He steps into the doorway of the Ark and prays.

Oh, great God, that art so good,
Men who have sinned will now be dead.
For all the world will sink in flood
Before my saddened sight.

He enters the Ark and after a brief pause looks out from the window.

This window I shall shutter now,
And to my chamber I shall go,

Until the rains and winds that blow
　　Abate, through the Lord's might.

He shuts the window.

End of Scene III

Scene IV

Noah opens the window of the Ark and looks around him.

NOAH　　Now forty days are come and gone.
　　I'll send a raven out anon

To see if any earth or stone
　　Be dry in any place.

He withdraws into the Ark and appears again in the doorway, with a raven. He sends the raven off stage. As it flies away, he continues.

If this bird come not again,
Then that will be a certain sign
That it is dry on hill or plain,
　　And God hath shown His Grace.

Noah waits for a short time, but the raven does not return.

Ah, Lord, wherever this raven be,
There land is dry. That I can see.

He withdraws into the Ark and returns to the doorway with a dove.

A dove, Lord, as a messenger
After him I shall send.

He speaks to the dove.

Do thou now return to me,
For of all birds that can fly
Thou art most meek and kind.

He sends off the dove. After a pause it returns with a branch of olive in its mouth. Noah rejoices.

Ah, Lord, blessèd be Thou for aye,
Who hath comforted me this day
By this bird.

Noah pauses and looks around the horizon.

I well may say
The flood appears to cease.
This dove hath brought a token of
The dear Lord's great and wondrous love,
A branch of olive from some far grove.
It is a sign of peace!

Noah holds the olive branch in his hand as he comes down from the Ark to the front of the stage. He falls to his knees as the Angel enters and climbs to the High Place.

ANGEL   Noah, take thy wife anon
And thy children, everyone.
From this ship you must be gone,
   And all of them with thee.
Animals and birds that fly,
To other regions they shall hie,
On earth to grow and multiply!
   He wills that this shall be.
Lord, I thank Thee for Thy power.
Thy word is done within the hour,
As fast as I can do, not slower.

He rises and bustles into the Ark, and comes out followed by his children. They return to the stage one by one, leading the beasts that they have taken in. Noah's Wife comes last, very meekly. After they have arranged themselves about the stage, Noah leads two of the larger animals to a spot directly below the High Place and prepares to sacrifice them. He takes a large knife from his belt and holds it up over his head as he speaks.

NOAH   Here, Lord, I do Thee honor
And to Thee offer sacrifice.
Of all these creatures Thou dost prize,
This day, Oh, Lordship ever wise,
   Thou to earth art Donor.

The Angel reaches down and catches his wrist. Noah drops his arm as the Angel speaks.

ANGEL   Noah, stay thy hand. For thou
Hast made a sacrifice enow
Already. God hath found thee true
And counteth thee His man.

Noah releases the beasts and falls to his knees. His family kneel also. The Angel continues speaking very gently.

The Lord will curse the earth no more
For man's ill deeds, which grieved him sore.
For man, from earliest days of yore,
 Has been inclined to sin.
A covenant with thee He will make,
And with thy children for thy sake,
His holy vengeance for to slake,
 For now He hath His own.
He giveth now His final word
To man and woman, beast and bird.
No more with flood shall the world be scoured.
 Mankind shall no more drown.

The Angel holds up a rainbow, pointing its arc toward the sky.

This bow, here between Him and thee,
In the firmament shall be
A token that thou mayest see
 That His wrath will cease,
That man or woman never more
Shall be wasted as before.
For worldliness that grieveth sore
 No longer master is.
Where clouds have in the heavens been,
This bow will ever more be seen
As witness that His wrath and spleen
 Will never shaken be.
The string of the bow is turned toward thee,
While bent toward Him the frame shall be.
No more toward earth can His arrows fly,
 He vows to thee this day.
His blessing now He giveth here
To thee, Noah, His servant dear.

His vengeance shall no more appear.
In Excelsis Gloria!

The Angel fixes the rainbow to the sky, descends from the High Place and leaves the stage. Noah and his family rise from their knees and very slowly, in couples, leave the stage, followed by the animals.

Curtain

Abraham and Isaac

From the Brome Play of ABRAHAM AND ISAAC

CAST *of* CHARACTERS

ABRAHAM, *an old man*	THE VOICE OF GOD
ISAAC, *his young son*	A DOCTOR
AN ANGEL	

Scene I

The scene is laid in the countryside near Abraham's home. Abraham and Isaac enter from one side and proceed slowly to the center downstage, Isaac following his father. Abraham pauses and speaks to God above in the heavens.

ABRAHAM

> Father of Heaven, omnipotent,
>> With all my heart to Thee I call.

Thou hast given me land and rent;
My livelihood Thou hast me sent.
  I thank Thee evermore for all.

First of our clay Thou madest Adam,
  And also Eve to be his wife;
All other creatures from these two came.
And now Thou dost grant to me, Abraham,
  Here in this land to lead my life.

In my old age Thou hast granted me this:
  That this young child to me was born.

He looks fondly at Isaac.

I love no thing so much, i-wiss,
Except Thyself, dear Father of Bliss,
  As Isaac here, my own sweet son.

Therefore, Father of Heaven, I pray
  Thee for his health and for his grace.
Dear Lord, keep him both night and day,
That never terror nor dismay
  Come to my child in any place.

Abraham turns and speaks to Isaac.

Come now, Isaac, my own sweet child,
Let us go home and take our rest.

ISAAC   Abraham, my father so mild,
I am always ready at your behest,
Both early and late.

ABRAHAM

Come then, sweet child. I love thee best
Of all the children I have begot.

Abraham continues across the stage, Isaac following him. Exeunt.

End of Scene I

Scene II

The scene is laid partly in Heaven, represented by the High Place at the back of the stage, and partly in the fields near Abraham's home, represented by the front portion of the stage. An Angel enters and slowly ascends to the High Place. He looks upward as the Voice of God is heard.

GOD'S VOICE

Mine angel, hie thee on thy way!
To middle earth thou shalt quickly go.
Abraham's heart will I test and try
Whether he be steadfast or no.

Say I command him for to take
Isaac, his son, that he loves so well,
And sacrifice of his blood to make,
If My love Abraham value still.

Show him the way unto the hill
Where his sacrifice shall be.

Now shall I test his loving will,
　If he love better his child or Me.
By his example he'll teach men all
　To honor their God and the Trinity.

*The Angel bows as the Voice of God is silent. Abraham enters
downstage and walks to the center, where he kneels in prayer. As
he prays, the Angel descends from the High Place and comes to
stand directly before Abraham, who is unaware of his presence.*

ABRAHAM

Now, Lord, That formed each living thing,
　My prayers I make to Thee again;
For this day my burnt-offering
　Here shall I make Thee on this plain.
Ah, Lord God, Almighty King,
　What sacrifice will make Thee fain?
If I could know what beast to bring,
　It should be brought with might and main,
　　Full soon anon.
To do Thy pleasure on a hill,

Verily, Lord, that is my will,
Dear Father, God in Trinity.

The Angel touches Abraham lightly on the shoulder. **Abraham**
starts.

ANGEL   Abraham! Abraham! Be thou blest!
Our Lord commandeth thee to take
Isaac, the son that thou lovest best,
And sacrifice of his blood to make.

Abraham freezes in horror.

Into the Land of Vision, go,
And offer thy child unto the Lord.
I shall lead thee and show thee so.

He pauses and points to the Mount in the distance backstage.

To God's word, Abraham, accord
And follow me upon this green.

Abraham stumbles to his feet. He speaks to the Angel respectfully,
but in obvious distress.

ABRAHAM   Welcome to me be my Lord's command.
His order I may not withstand.
Yet Isaac, the youngest of my band,
A full dear child to me has been.

I had liefer, if God were pleased,
To lose all the lands and goods I have
Than that Isaac my son should be roughly used —
As God in Heaven my soul may save!

On earth no thing is to me so dear,
And now I must the young child kill.
Ah, Lord! My heart doth strongly stir!
And yet, dear Lord, I do sorely fear

To grudge Thee anything of Thy will!

I love my child as I love my life;
  But yet I love my God much more.
For Thee my heart would suffer strife.
I will not spare it for child nor wife,
  But follow my Lord's commandment here.

Though I love my son Isaac never so well,
  I must indeed smite off his head!
Ah, Father of Heaven! To Thee I kneel!
A hard, hard death my son shall feel
  To honor Thee, our Lord and God.

Abraham kneels and buries his head in his robes to hide his anguish. The Angel speaks to him gently.

ANGEL   Abraham! Abraham! Thou hast well said!
  That this commandment thou shalt obey.
But in thy heart be not dismayed!

Abraham lifts his head with resignation.

ABRAHAM
  Nay, nay, I hold me well arrayed
  To please my God as best I may.

The Angel leaves him and ascends the High Place. Abraham rises to his feet and speaks as he walks wearily toward the exit.

For though my heart be heavily set
  To shed the blood of my own dear son,
Yet for all this I will not doubt,
But Isaac my son I will go fetch out,
  And come again as fast as we can.

Abraham turns sadly away. Exit.

End of Scene II

Scene III

The scene is laid near Abraham's home. Isaac is kneeling at one downstage corner. Abraham enters opposite and crosses over to him, walking sadly. As he walks, he speaks as though he could not see the boy.

ABRAHAM

    Now, Isaac, my own son so dear,
        Where art thou, child? Come, speak to me.

ISAAC   Father, sweet father, I am here,
        Making my prayers to the Trinity.

Abraham sees him.

ABRAHAM

    Rise up, my child, and fast come hither,
        My gentle bairn that art so wise.
    For we two, child, must go together
        And unto the Lord make sacrifice.

Isaac rises and runs cheerfully to his father.

ISAAC   I am full ready, my father, so!
        Beside you, see, I stand right here;
    And whatsoever ye bid me do,
        It shall be done with merry cheer,
        Full well and fine.

ABRAHAM

    Ah! Isaac, my own young son so dear,
        I give thee both God's blessing and mine!

He picks up a bundle of faggots which are lying at the edge of the stage.

    Take these faggots upon thy back.

He places the bundle on Isaac's back, and himself picks up a lamp which contains a coal to start the fire for the sacrifice.

> And I myself the fire shall bring.

ISAAC   Father, this wood I will gladly pack;
> I am ready at your bidding.

Abraham turns away to hide his tears.

ABRAHAM
> Ah, Lord of Heaven! My hands I wring,
> This child's words truly wound my heart.

He speaks again to Isaac.

> Now, Isaac, let us go on our way
> Unto yon mountain, with all our main.

Abraham points to the mountain in the distance.

ISAAC   Go we, dear father, as fast as we may.
> To follow you I am full fain,
> Though I be slender.

ABRAHAM   *aside*
> Ah, Lord! My heart doth break in twain —
> This child's words, they be so tender.

Abraham leads the way sadly, while Isaac follows cheerfully, as they begin their journey to the mountain.

End of Scene III

Scene IV

The scene is laid on the mountain in the Land of Vision. In the center of the mountain is an altar for sacrifice. On at least one side of the "foot" of the mountain is a thicket of shrubs. The Angel stands quietly in the High Place. Abraham and Isaac enter wearily, carrying the faggots and the lamp, as though they have come a long journey. They "climb" the mountain and stand on either side of it.

ABRAHAM

> Ah, Isaac, son, lay the faggots down;
>> No longer bear on thy back this wood.
> For I must make all ready anon
>> To honor my Lord God as I should.

Isaac lays his bundle down at the foot of the altar.

ISAAC   Lo, Father Abraham, there it is!
>> To please you always to me is dear.

He looks quizzically at his father.

> But, father, I marvel sore at this:
>> Why do ye make this heavy cheer?

Isaac shudders slightly, as though he feels some unexplained fear.

> And also, father, I feel afraid!
>> Where is the beast that ye should kill?
> We have ready both fire and wood,
>> But of living beasts there is none on this hill!

A living beast I know there must be
Before the sacrifice you can make.

ABRAHAM

Fear thee not, son, I counsel thee.
Our Lord will send here unto me
Some manner of beast for us to take
By his command.

Abraham has turned his face away as he speaks. He draws his sword from its sheath as he finishes. Isaac becomes more alarmed and shrinks away slightly.

ISAAC   But, father, my heart begins to quake
To see that sharp sword in your hand!

Why carry ye your sword drawn so?
At your dark frown I have much wonder.

Abraham turns away in great distress.

ABRAHAM

Ah, Father of Heaven, I'm bent with woe!
This child here breaks my heart asunder!

ISAAC   Tell me, dear father, ere that ye cease,
Bear ye your sword thus drawn for me?

ABRAHAM

Ah, Isaac, sweet son! Have peace! Have peace!
For surely thou breakest my heart in three!

Isaac is still frightened and bewildered, but gathers some courage to approach more closely to his father.

ISAAC   Truly some trouble ye dismays,
That ye mourn ever thus more and more.

ABRAHAM *aside*

> Ah, Lord of Heaven! Let fall Thy grace!
> My heart was never half so sore.

ISAAC　　I pray you, father, let me know well,
　　　　　If I shall come to harm or no.

ABRAHAM

> As yet, sweet son, I may not tell:
> My heart is now so full of woe.

Isaac falls to his knees and tugs at his father's cloak, begging him.

ISAAC　　Dear father, I pray, hide not from me
　　　　　Your thought, but surely tell your son.

Abraham straightens himself and looks away. He speaks grimly.

ABRAHAM

> Isaac! Isaac! I must kill thee.

Isaac starts back, horrified.

ISAAC　　Kill me? Father, what have I done?

> If I have trespassed against you in aught,
> With a rod ye may beat me till I be mild.

But with your sharp sword kill me not!
For, father, indeed I am but a child.

Abraham turns to him and speaks with great sadness.

ABRAHAM

I am bowed with sorrow thy blood to spill,
But truly, my child, I have no choice.

ISAAC   Now I wish my mother were on this hill!
She would kneel for me on both her knees
To save my life!
But since my mother is nowhere near,
I beg you, father, change your cheer,
And kill me not with your sharp knife!

ABRAHAM

Forsooth, my son, unless I thee kill,
I shall grieve God right sore, I dread.
It is His commandment, it is His will,
That I should do this dreadful deed.

He ordered me, for certain, son,
To make my sacrifice with thy blood.

Isaac begins to realize his father's meaning. He speaks faintly.

ISAAC   And is it God's will that I be slain?

ABRAHAM   Yea, truly, Isaac, my child so good!
And, therefore, sorely my hands I wring.

Forsooth, son, unless I do this deed,
Sorely displeased our Lord will be.

*Isaac summons up his courage to face his necessity. He speaks
sadly.*

ISAAC   Nay, nay, father! God forbid
      That ever ye should grieve Him for me.

You have more children, one or two,
    Whom you should love as well as I.
I pray you, father, make no woe;
For you will forget me as soon as I go.
    Out of mind I shall quickly fly.

Therefore, do thou our Lord's command,
    And when I am dead, then pray for me.
But tell ye my mother nought of my end.
Say I am living in another land.

Abraham is deeply touched at Isaac's thoughtfulness.

ABRAHAM   Ah, Isaac! Isaac! Blessed may thou be!

ISAAC   But, father, ere I go to my death,
      I pray you, bless me with your hand!

*He kneels before his father, who places his hands on the boy's
head.*

ABRAHAM

    Now, Isaac, my son, with all my breath,
      My blessing I give thee upon this land,
        And may our God give thee His grace!

He reaches down and takes Isaac's hands.

    Isaac, Isaac, do thou stand,
      That once again I may thee embrace.

They embrace. Isaac turns away.

ISAAC   Now, farewell, my own father so wise;
      And bear to my mother a greeting word.

> But I pray you, father, to hide mine eyes,
> That I may not see the stroke of your sword.

ABRAHAM

> Child, thy words make me to weep full sore.
> Now, dear son Isaac, speak no more.

Isaac stands with his back to his father, as Abraham turns and moves to the opposite corner of the mountain, wringing his hands. After a pause, Isaac turns toward him.

ISAAC   But truly, father, all this tarrying
> Doth my heart no good, but harm.

Abraham turns slowly and beckons Isaac to come to him. They meet before the altar.

> I pray you, make a speedy ending.

ABRAHAM   Come forward, sweet son, unto my arm.

He takes a rope from his belt and starts to bind Isaac's arms behind his back.

> For I must bind thy body, too.
> Although thou be never so mild.

ISAAC   *crying out*

> Ah, Mercy, father! Why should you do so?

ABRAHAM   That thou shouldst not hinder me, my child.

Isaac tries to pull away.

ISAAC   Nay, surely, father, I will not stop you.
> I will not hinder you in your will.
> And this high purpose that you have set you,
> For God's love, keep it before thee still.

He submits meekly to the binding. As Abraham continues to bind him, he speaks gently.

But father, I pray you evermore
   That to my mother you nothing tell.
If she knew, she would weep full sore,
   For surely, father, she loved me well.
      God's blessing may she have!

Isaac cries out.

Now, fare thee well, my mother so sweet!
We two be like no more to meet.

ABRAHAM

Ah, Isaac! Thou makest my heart to break,
   And with thy words thou piercest me.

ISAAC   Ah, sweet father, I am sorry to grieve you.
   I cry you mercy for all I have done,
For all my trespass that ever did move you.
   Now, father, forgive me for what I have done.
      God of Heaven be with me!

Abraham finishes the binding, and lifts Isaac onto the altar.

ABRAHAM

Isaac, my dear son, here shalt thou lie!

He speaks with grim determination.

Unto my work I must me set.
I had as lief myself to die.
   Would God were pleased with me instead,
   And my own body as offer!

ISAAC   Ah, mercy, father! Mourn ye no more!
Your weeping maketh my heart as sore
   As the death that I shall suffer.

But wind your kerchief about my eyes!

Abraham leans over him very gently. He takes a kerchief and binds it around Isaac's eyes.

ABRAHAM   I shall, my sweet child, follow thy word.

ISAAC   Now, still, good father, I pray you this!
    Smite me not often with your sharp sword,
     But quickly let it be sped.

ABRAHAM
    Now farewell, my child, so full of grace!

ISAAC   *crying out in fear*
    Ah, father! Father! Turn downward my face,
     For of your sharp sword I am adread.

Abraham gently turns him over face downward, then turns away from the altar.

ABRAHAM
    Lo! Now is the time come, 'tis plain,
     When my sharp sword in his neck must bite.
    Lord God! My heart faileth here again;
     I cannot find it in my heart to smite.
      My courage will not rise thereto.
    Gladly would I work my Father's will.
    But this young innocent lies so still,
    I find it not in my heart to kill.

He cries out in anguish.

    Oh, Father of Heaven, what shall I do?

ISAAC   Have mercy, father! Why tarry ye so,
    And let me lie so long on this heath?
    I would to God the stroke had cut through!

> Father, I pray you, shorten my woe,
>> And let me not long thus for my death!

As Abraham speaks, the Angel quietly descends from the High Place and stands directly behind him, without his knowledge.

ABRAHAM

> Heart, why dost thou not break in three?
>> Yet shall I do what must be done.

He walks slowly to stand beside the altar.

> I will no longer stop for thee,
>> For thus my God aggrieved would be.

He raises his sword, ready to strike.

> Now take the stroke, my own dear son!

As he starts to bring his sword down for the stroke, the Angel grasps his arm. The sword falls to the ground, and Abraham steps back in wonder.

ANGEL   I am an angel, as thou mayest see,
That from Heaven is sent to thee.
Our Lord a hundred times thanketh thee.
   His commandment thou hast kept.

He knows thee well, and He knows thy heart,
   That thou lovest Him above everything!
That some of thy sorrow may depart,
   A fair ram yonder to thee I bring.

The Angel points to the thicket.

Lo, it stands tethered to a briar.
   Now, Abraham, amend thy mood,
For Isaac, thy son, that lies on the fire,
   This day shall shed no drop of his blood.

Go! Make thy sacrifice with yon ram.
Now, farewell, blessed Abraham!
For unto Heaven I now go home.
   Take up thy son so free!

Abraham remains frozen in his place, while the Angel turns and ascends to the High Place. Then Abraham falls to his knees in front of the altar.

ABRAHAM
Dear Lord, I thank Thee for Thy great grace.
Now am I eased in many ways.

He rises and bends over Isaac. He speaks excitedly.

Isaac, rise up! Dear son, arise!
   Rise up, sweet child, and come to me.

Isaac, still unaware of the miracle, cries piteously.

ISAAC   Ah, mercy, father! Why smite ye not?
   Ah! Smite on, father, once with your knife!

Abraham takes the kerchief off Isaac's head, and fumbles with his bonds, as he speaks joyously.

ABRAHAM

> Peace, my sweet son! And fear thee nought!
>> Our Lord of Heaven hath spared thy life
>>> Through His Angel now.
> Truly, this day thou shalt not die!

Isaac sits up slowly and stiffly, rubbing his arms. He is still fearful.

ISAAC   Ah, father! Full glad indeed were I —
> If but, father . . . I say . . . if this . . .
> If this tale were true.

ABRAHAM   *in great excitement*

> My son, a hundred times for joy
>> Thyself will I now embrace.

Abraham lifts Isaac from the altar and embraces him. Isaac still holds himself stiffly, not understanding Abraham's joy.

ISAAC   Ah, my dear father Abraham,
> Will not God be angry that we do thus?

ABRAHAM

> No, no! Sweet son! For yonder same ram
> He hath sent by an Angel from Heaven, His home,
>> Hither down to us.

> Yon beast shall die here in thy stead,
>> In worship of our Lord alone.
> Go. Fetch him hither, my child, with speed.

As Abraham is speaking, Isaac begins to realize the miracle of his deliverance. He relaxes and his face lights up with joy.

ISAAC　　Father, I will catch him by the head
　　　　　And bring him back with me anon.

Isaac runs to the thicket and sees the ram. He speaks to it as he is untying it.

　　　　Ah! Sheep! Sheep! Blessed may thou be,
　　　　　That ever thou were sent down hither!
　　　　Thou shalt this day die for me
　　　　In worship of Holy Trinity.
　　　　　Now, come along fast! Go we together
　　　　　To my Father in Heaven.

He picks up the sheep, or leads it, from the thicket. He speaks to it as he brings it to the mountaintop.

　　　　Though thou art never so gentle and good,
　　　　Yet had I liefer thou sheddest thy blood,
　　　　　Indeed, sheep, than I.

Isaac brings the sheep to his father.

　　　　Lo, father, I have brought here full smart
　　　　　This gentle ram that to you I give.

He pauses and turns toward the High Place.

　　　　Lord God, I thank thee with all my heart,
　　　　　For I am full glad that I shall live
　　　　　And kiss once more my mother.

Abraham comes to him.

ABRAHAM
　　　　Now be right merry, my sweet child,
　　　　For this live beast, that is so mild,
　　　　　Here shall I offer before all other.

Abraham attends to the ram, while Isaac fetches a bellows from behind the altar and holds it ready to fan the fire.

ISAAC   And I will fast begin to blow.
    This fire shall burn at a full good speed.

He pauses, and looks quizzically at Abraham for a moment.

    But, father, if I should stoop down low,
    You will not smite with your sword, I trow?

Abraham lifts his sword, which he has drawn to prepare for the sacrifice; then he laughs at Isaac's worried look.

ABRAHAM   No, hardly, sweet son! Have thee no dread.
    My distress is past.

Isaac still looks at the sword with distaste.

ISAAC   Yet I wish that sword were melted indeed.
    For, father, it makes me still aghast!

Abraham places the sheep on the altar and makes the sacrifice. As he does so, he prays. Isaac kneels beside the altar.

ABRAHAM

    Now, Lord God of Heaven in Trinity,
        Almighty God omnipotent,
    My offering I make in worship of Thee,
        With this gentle beast which I present.
        Oh, Lord! Receive Thou mine intent,
            As Thou art God and Source of our grace.

As Abraham completes his prayer, he bows his head. The Angel speaks from the High Place.

ANGEL   Abraham, Abraham, God will thee speed,
        And Isaac, thy son, that stands thee by!
    Truly, Abraham, for this deed
    The Lord shall multiply your seed
        As thick as stars be in the sky,
            Both more and less.

As thick as gravel in the sea,
So multiplied your seed shall be,
 For your goodness.

Of you shall come forth many a one
 To live in bliss without an end,
For ye dread Him as God alone,
And keep His commandments every one.
 His blessing He gives, wheresoe'er ye wend.

*The Angel descends from the High Place, while Abraham and
Isaac remain with their heads bowed. The Angel leaves the stage.
When he is gone, Abraham and Isaac rouse themselves. Slowly
they "climb" down the mountain to the stage proper. As they
walk, Abraham speaks.*

ABRAHAM

 Lo, Isaac, my dear son, what think ye
  About this work that we have wrought?
 Full glad and merry may we be,
  The will of God that we grudged not,
   On this fair heath.

ISAAC   Ah, father! I thank the Lord of All

My foolish wit served me so well —
    To fear God more than to fear my death.

Abraham turns and lays his hand on Isaac's shoulder.

ABRAHAM

Why, dear son, wert thou afraid?
    Quickly, child, tell me thy fear.

ISAAC   Yea, father, I was sore in dread.
    I was never so afraid before,
        As I have been on yonder hill.

He turns to look at the mountain, then shudders.

But by my faith, father, I swear,
I will nevermore go there,
    Except against my will.

Abraham smiles at him reassuringly.

ABRAHAM

Yea! Come now with me, my own sweet son,
And homeward quickly let us be gone.

ISAAC   Indeed, father, I'll gladly come.
    I was never so eager to see my home
        And to speak with my dear mother.

They come together to the center of the stage. Abraham pauses.

ABRAHAM

Lord of Heaven, I give thanks to Thee,
That now I may lead home with me
Isaac, my youngest son, so free,
    The gentlest child above all other.

He turns to Isaac, and starts to lead him off.

Now, go we forth, my blessed son.

ISAAC   With all my heart, father, let us be gone.
        For by my troth, were I once at home,
        I would never wish to go out therefrom!

Isaac turns to face the audience.

        God grant us forever His grace, and do so
        To all these that we be beholden to.

He gestures to the audience, then follows Abraham off stage.

End of Scene IV

Epilogue

*Enter a Doctor, who comes to the center of the stage and speaks
directly to the audience.*

DOCTOR   Lo, sovereigns and sires! Now have we showed
        This solemn story to great and small.
        It is a good lesson for learned and crude,
          And for the wisest of us all,
            Throughout the land.
        For this story showeth you plainly here
        How we should keep, to the best of our power,
          God's own command.

        Think ye, sirs, if God sent an Angel
          And ordered you your child to kill,
        By your troth, is there anyone of you here
          That would grudge or strive against His will?
          How think ye now, sirs, thereby?

        I trow there be three or four or so
          Of these women that weep so sorrowfully,

When that their children from them die —
　　It is the nature of their kind.
It is but folly, I may well avow,
To grudge God's will, or to grieve thereto,
For He'll not be mischieved, well I know,
　　By land or water. Bear this in mind.

Do not cry out against our God,
　　In wealth or woe, whatever He send,
Though you be never so hard downtrod.
　　For when He will, He may it amend.
His commandments keep with all good will,
　　As this tale hath shown, that ye may learn,
And faithfully serve Him with heart and soul,
　　That ye may please God both evening and morn.

　　Now Jesus, That weareth the Crown of Thorn,
　　　　Bring us all to Heaven's bliss!

Exit the Doctor.

Curtain

The Nativity

From the York NATIVITY Play

CAST of CHARACTERS

MARY   JOSEPH

The scene is laid outside a stable in Bethlehem. The stable is dark-ened at the opening of the play, but later will be lighted to provide the traditional Manger setting for Mary and the Christ Child. Enter Mary and Joseph wearily. They see the stable. Mary waits down-stage while Joseph examines the shed, then he comes to the front of the stage and prays.

JOSEPH   Almighty God in Trinity,
        I pray Thee, Lord, in Thy great might,
        Look down. Thy simple servant see.
        Here in this place where we are brought,
           Weak and alone,

Grant us a resting place this night
    Within this town.

For we have sought both up and down,
Through diverse streets of this city!
So many people are come to town
That we can find no hostelry.
    There is such a rabble,
Forsooth, no other help I see
    But this poor stable.

Joseph goes backstage, enters the dark stable, and looks it over carefully. He returns discouraged. He points out its defects to Mary as he speaks to her.

If we here all night abide,
The storm will blow upon us still.
The walls are down on every side;
The roof is open to rain and hail
    Above, I trow.
Say, Mary daughter, what is thy will?
    What shall we do?

For now are we in grievous need,
As thou thyself the sooth may see;
For here is neither blanket nor bed,
And we are weak and both weary,
  And fain would rest.

He turns away from her and prays again.

Now, gracious God, in Thy mercy,
  Show what is best!

Mary comes over to Joseph and speaks to him quietly and with confidence.

MARY   God will guide us, full well know ye!
        Therefore, Joseph, be of good cheer.

In this same place born will He be
That shall us save from sorrows sore,
  Both night and morn.
Sir, know ye well, the time is near
  When He will be born.

JOSEPH Then it behooves us bide here still,
        Here in this same place all this night.

MARY Yea, forsooth, that is God's will.

Joseph looks at her gently, then starts to make the stable comfortable, determined to make the best of things.

JOSEPH Then would I fain we had some light,
    Whatever befall.
It grows right dark unto my sight,
    And cold withal.

I will go get us light therefore,
And find some fuel to make a fire.

MARY Almighty God go you before,
As He is Sovereign of all things here,
    In His great power!
May He lend me grace now to prepare
    For this His hour!

Joseph leaves the stage. Mary enters the stable. There is a pause. The outer stage is darkened, if possible, and suddenly the interior of the stable is lighted, to show Mary seated beside the manger, holding the Child in her lap. She worships Him.

Hail! My Lord God! Hail, Prince of Peace!
Hail, my Father! And hail, my Son!
Hail, Sovereign Liege, all sins to cease!
Hail, God and Man, dwelling in One!
   Hail, Thou, through Whose might
All this world was first begun,
    Darkness and Light!

Son, as I am subject of Thine,
Vouchsafe, sweet Son, now here I pray Thee,
That I may hold Thee in these arms of mine,
And in these poor weeds to array Thee.
   Grant me but this,
As I am chosen Thy mother to be
   In truthfulness!

She wraps her cloak about the Baby. Joseph enters downstage, carrying a lantern and some wood. He does not see the scene in the stable, but speaks directly to the audience.

JOSEPH   Ah! Lord in Heaven! The weather is cold!
The fearfulest freeze that I ever did feel!
I pray God give succor to them that are old,
And also to them that may be unwell,
   So I may say.
Now, God, be Thou my Shelter still,
   As best Thou may!

A star blazes out above the stable. Joseph sees it and is startled.

Ah, Lord of All! What light is this
That comes shining thus suddenly?
I cannot say, as I have bliss!
When I have brought this wood to Mary
   Then shall I inquire.

He turns and sees the stable.

Thanks be to God, the place I see.

He enters the stable.

MARY   Ye are welcome, sir!

Joseph speaks as he puts down the lantern and the wood.

JOSEPH   Tell me, Mary daughter, how farest thee?

MARY   Right well, Joseph, as has been aye.

Joseph straightens up and suddenly seems to realize what has happened.

JOSEPH   O, Mary! What sweet Thing is on thy knee?

MARY   It is my Son, the sooth to say,
             That is so mild.

Joseph falls to his knees in wonder.

JOSEPH   Blessed am I, who am bade this day
             To see this Child.

He worships for a moment, then half rises and looks about him.

I marvel mickle at this light
That shineth thus throughout this place.
Forsooth, it is a wondrous sight!

MARY   This has He ordained of His grace,
      My Son and King,
That a star be shining for a space
      At His bearing.

For Balaam long ago foretold
How that full high should rise a star;
And of a maid should be born a Child,
A Son, that shall be our Saviour
      From cares unkind.
Forsooth, it is my Son so free
      Balaam bore in mind.

JOSEPH   Now, welcome, Flower of fairest hue!
I shall Thee worship with main and might.
Hail, my Maker! Hail, Christ Jesu!
Hail, royal King, Root of all right!
   Hail, Saviour!
Hail, my Lord, Lender of light!
   Hail, blessed Flower!

MARY   *speaking to the Child*
Now, Lord, That all this world shall win —
To Thee, my Son, this must I say, —
Here is no cradle to lay Thee in.
Therefore, my dear Son, I Thee pray,
   Since it is so,
That in this crib I may Thee lay,
   Between beasts two.

She lays the Child in the manger very gently and wraps the cloak about Him.

And I shall wrap Thee, my own dear Child,
With such poor clothes as we may have.

As Mary is attending to the Child, Joseph looks behind the manger. He turns and speaks to her in amazement.

JOSEPH   O Mary, behold these creatures mild!
They make devotions, loving and grave,
   As if they were men!
Forsooth, it seems well and clearly told
   That their Lord they ken.

MARY   Their Lord they ken, that know I well;
They worship Him with might and main.
The weather is cold, as ye may feel.

To cherish Him they are full fain.
　　With their breath warm
They breathe upon Him, this may you tell,
　　To keep Him from harm!

Mary looks back into the crib.

　　O, now sleeps my Son! Blest may He be!
　　He lies full warm these beasts between.

JOSEPH　Thus is fulfilled, forsooth I see,
　　What Habakkuk long ago did mean
　　　　In his prophesying.

　　He said our Saviour should be seen
　　　　Between beasts lying.

　　And now I see the same in sight.

MARY　Yea, forsooth, the same is He.

JOSEPH　Honor and worship both day and night,
　　Eternal Lord, be done to Thee,
　　　　As it is worthy.
　　And, Lord, to Thy service I promise me
　　　　With my heart wholly.

Joseph steps back from the crib and falls to his knees. Mary speaks in prayer, very slowly and clearly.

MARY   Thou merciful Maker, God on High,
       Lord of Heaven, my Son so free,
       Thy handmaiden, forsooth, am I;
       And to Thy service I promise me,
           With all my heart and mind.
       And, Son, Thy blessing, beseech I Thee,
           Thou grant to us, all mankind!

Curtain

The Shepherds' Play

From SECUNDA PASTORUM, *of the Wakefield Cycle*

CAST *of* CHARACTERS

COLL, *a shepherd*   GILL, *Mak's wife*

GIB, *a shepherd*   AN ANGEL

DAW, *a young shepherd*   THE VIRGIN *and the Infant*

MAK, *a thief*   *Jesus*

Scene I

The scene is laid on the moors near Horbury in Yorkshire, on a winter's night. Coll, the first shepherd, enters, blowing on his hands and shivering with cold. He walks about the stage talking to himself.

COLL   Lord, these weathers are cold! And I am ill wrapped.
I am near dead, it's so long since I've napped.

My legs they fold. My fingers are chapped.
Things are not as I'd have them, for I am all lapped
   In sorrow!
In storm and tempest —
Now in the East, now in the West —
Woe to him who can never rest,
   Midday nor morrow!

He comes to the center of the stage and speaks to the audience.

We poor wretched farmers that walk on the moor,
In faith, we are driven near out of the door.
It is not a wonder that we be so poor,
For the tilth of our land lies as dry as the floor,
   As ye ken.
We are so crossed,
Overtaxed and oppressed —
We are bound hard and fast
   By these gentlemen!

First there comes a fellow as proud as a po!
He will borrow my wagon, my plow also.
And I am full willing to lend, so he'll go!

He shakes his head sadly.

Thus live we in pain, anger and woe,
   By night and day.
He must have what he sues.
If I should refuse,
I should hang in a noose
   Should I once say him Nay.

He sighs and walks about.

It does my heart good, as I walk thus alone,

Of this world to talk, in a manner of moan.
To my sheep I shall go, and hearken anon.
There rest on a hillock or sit on a stone,
   Full soon!

He catches sight of someone approaching.

For I trow, perdee,
True men if they be,
We'll get more company
   Ere it be noon.

*Coll moves to the back of the stage, out of sight of Gib, the second
shepherd, who enters lamenting.*

GIB   *Benedicite* and *Dominus!* What does it all mean?
       Why fares the world thus? What have we not seen?
       Lord, these winds are spiteful, and the storms so
          keen,
       And the frosts so sharp, they water mine een,
         'Tis no lie!
       Now in dry, now in wet,
       Now in snow, now in sleet:
       When my shoes freeze to my feet,
         It is not all easy!

He comes forward and speaks to the audience.

Now as far as I ken, or yet as I go,
We poor married men suffer much woe!
We have sorrow, I tell you! It often falls so.

He flaps his arms and imitates a chicken cackling.

> Old Capelle, our hen, both to and fro
>   She cackles.

He pauses.

> But begin she to croak,
> To groan or to cluck —
> Then woe to our cock,
>   For he is in shackles!

> You young men, of wooing, lest that ye be caught,
> Be wary of wedding — and think in your thought!
> "Had I wist!" is a saying that serves us of nought.
> For mickle of mourning has a wedding-day brought
>   And of grief
> In many a sharp shower!
> You may catch in an hour
> What you'll savor full sour
>   As long as you live!

> As I've read the Epistle, I've one for my dear
> As sharp as a thistle, as rough as a briar!
> She is browed like a bristle; she has a sour cheer.
> If she once wets her whistle, she can sing full clear
>   Her Pater Noster.
> She's as great as a whale.
> She has a gallon of gall.
> I say to you all,
>   I wish I had lost her.

Coll steps forward.

COLL   Look over the row! Full deafly ye stand!

Gib jumps at the sound of his voice.

GIB   The Devil lurks in thy mouth like a brand!

He recovers himself.

   Saw thou anywhere Daw?

COLL   Yea, on a lea land
  I heard him blow. He comes here at hand
    Not far.

Coll peers off stage and motions to Gib to be quiet.

   Stand still.

GIB   Why?

COLL For he comes, hope I.

GIB   He will tell us both a lie
    Unless we beware.

*They move backstage. Enter Daw, the young shepherd. He thinks
himself alone.*

DAW Never since Noah's flood were such floods seen,
   Winds and rains so rude, and storms so keen!
   Folk stammer and chatter with fear, as I ween.
   May God turn all to good! I say as I mean.
    But ponder!
   These floods they drown
   Both in fields and in town,
   And bear all down.
    And that is a wonder!
   We that walk through the nights, our cattle to keep,
   We see sudden sights when other men sleep.

He notices the other two, but does not greet them.

   Yet methink my heart lights! I see rascals peep.
   They are two tall wights!

He turns to go off stage away from them.

I'll look to my sheep.

But, no!

He checks himself.

> 'Tis a foolish intent.
> As I walk on this bent,
> I may lightly repent
> > If I stub my toe.

He turns to the other shepherds. He greets Coll and then his master Gib, both of whom step forward.

> Ah, sir, God save you, and you, master mine!
> A drink would I have, and somewhat to dine.

COLL   A curse on thee, knave. Thou art a sorry hind!

GIB   How the boy likes to rave! 'Tis not yet the time.

To Daw

> We've no food.

> Ill thrift on thy pate!

To Coll

> Though the rascal came late,
> Yet is he in state
> > To dine if he could.

Daw shrugs his shoulders and turns directly to the audience.

DAW   Such servants as I, that sweat and swink,
> Can eat our bread dry, and that makes me think.
> We are oft wet and weary, while our mastermen
> > wink.

Yet comes very late both our dinner and drink.
   Nevertheless,
Our dame and our sire,
When we've run in the mire,
They nip at our hire,
   And pay us amiss.

To Gib

I say the truth, master! For the profit you make,
I do accordingly, work as I like!
I get but little, and everything lack —
For yet came my supper not once to my sack
   In the field.

He dances about with mock lightheartedness.

But why should I peep?
With my staff I can leap.
"A bargain that's cheap
   Gives a poor yield!"

COLL   You're a stupid lad to keep on depending
   On a poor herdsman with little of spending.

GIB   Peace, boy, I bid thee! No more complaining.
   Or I'll make thee smart with a blow, for the mending
      Of thy gauds.
   Where are the sheep we've shorn?

DAW   Sir, this same day at morn
   I left them in the corn
      When they rang Lauds.

   They have pasture good. They cannot go wrong.

COLL   That is right, as he says.

He yawns and stretches.

>Ah, these nights are long!
>Yet I wish, ere we went, someone gave us a song.

GIB   I think as you do. It would cheer us along!

DAW   That I grant.

COLL   Let me sing the tenory.

GIB   And I the treble so high!

DAW   Then the mean falls to me.

>Let's see how you chant!

They make several attempts to find a good pitch, when Daw puts his finger to his lips and points off stage. They step back quietly for a moment as Mak enters stealthily. He has a cloak thrown over his shoulder. They let him creep to the middle of the stage, then they confront him. He straightens up with great dignity and pretends not to know them.

Gib steps up first.

GIB   Mak, whence have you come? Tell us thy tidings.

DAW   Is Mak come? Then take care for your things!

Daw runs behind Mak and snatches the cloak off his shoulder. He shows it to the others and to the audience to indicate that it really is his cloak, which Mak had stolen. Mak draws himself up very indignantly and turns to Daw.

MAK What? I am a yeoman, I tell you — the king's!
  The self and same, sent from great lordings
    And so on.

The three shepherds gather around him so that he is surrounded. He stands very stiffly and gestures to them with distaste.

MAK Fie on you! Go hence,
  Out of my presence!
  I must have reverence.
    Am I not known?

COLL Why act ye so quaint, Mak? Ye do wrong.

GIB *You* play the saint, Mak? You lie all along.

DAW The rascal can paint so, the devil might him hang!

Mak turns angrily to them.

MAK I shall make complaint, and make you all thwang
    With a whip!
  I'll tell just what ye doth!

Coll steps closer and shakes his finger in Mak's face.

COLL But, Mak, is that the truth?
  Now take out that Southern tooth
    And mend your lip.

Gib steps up and threatens to strike Mak on the head.

GIB Mak, open your eye! I'll make you see clear.

Daw steps up and jeers in Mak's face. Mak is completely surrounded and his knees are shaking.

DAW   Mak, know ye not me? I could trouble you sore!

Mak looks at them in terror, then pretends that he is recognizing them for the first time.

MAK   God bless you! Methought I had seen you before.
            Ye are a good company!

The three shepherds step back away from him, satisfied. He smirks at them.

COLL   Now do you speak fair!

GIB   Rascal! Jape!
            Thus late as thou goes,
            What will men suppose?
            Thou hast an ill gloss
                For the stealing of sheep.

Mak protests indignantly.

MAK   I am as true as steel. All men know it!

He changes his tune and moves away from them, holding his stomach as if he were in sudden pain.

            But a sickness I feel that keeps me full hot.
            My belly fares not well. It is out of estate.

DAW   Seldom lies the Devil dead by the gate!

MAK   Therefore
            Full sore I am and ill,
            Though I stand stone-still.
            I've not eaten a morsel
                This month or more.

The shepherds grimace at each other to show their disbelief.

COLL   How fares thy wife? By my hood, how fares Gill?

Mak shrugs his shoulders and walks away, shaking his head.

MAK   She lies rolling about by the fire, withal
         She has a house full of children. She drinks very
             well.
         But whatever else that she touches fares ill.
           She
         Eats as fast as she can;
         And each year that comes to man,
         She brings forth a little one,
           And some years two!

The shepherds look amused at Mak's lament. Then Coll begins to shiver, and he speaks to his friends.

COLL   I am cold and naked, and would have a fire!

GIB   I wot so weary there's none in this shire!

He stretches.

         I must sleep, though I earn even less for my hire.

He rolls his cloak about him and prepares to lie down.

DAW   I am worn from walking, and run in the mire.

He motions to Gib.

         Watch thou!

Gib shakes his head at Daw and sits down.

GIB   Nay, I will lie down by,
         For I must sleep truly.

Gib yawns. Coll lies down not far from Gib, leaving room for the others between them. Daw looks at them reproachfully.

DAW   As good a man's son am I
         As any of you.

Daw looks quizzically at Mak, then has a good idea.

But, Mak, come hither! Between us you shall rest!

Mak looks back slyly and speaks sarcastically.

MAK   Then might I overhear the news that you'd list
           To whisper!

Daw confidently takes Mak's arm and makes him lie down between Coll and Gib. Then Daw lies down beside him. As they settle down, Mak says his prayers.

    "From my top to my toe,
    Manus tuas commendo,
    Pontio Pilato:
       The Lord let us prosper!"

They all go to sleep. Mak pretends to snore for a moment, then rises and listens to their breathing. When he is sure they are asleep, he tiptoes to the front of the stage and speaks confidentially to the audience.

    Now 'tis time for a man that lacks what he would
    To creep very quietly into the fold,
    And nimbly to work then — and be not too bold,
    For he might rue the bargain, if it were told
       At the ending.
    Now were time for to steal.

But he needs good counsel
That fain would eat well
   And has but little spending.

Mak turns back to the others and works a spell over them.

About you a circle as round as a moon
Cast now I will. Until it be noon
Ye will lie stone-still to all that I do.
And I shall say here of good words a few.

He chants.

"On hight
Over your heads my hand I lift.
Out go your eyes, both right and left!"

Thoughtfully to himself.

But yet must I make better shrift,
   If this be right!

He watches the sleeping shepherds for a moment, then turns to the audience.

Now they sleep hard! That ye may be sure.
I was never a shepherd, but I will learn here.
Though the flock be frightened, yet shall I nip.

He tiptoes off stage momentarily, and is heard from the wings.

How! Draw hither! Now mends our cheer
   From sorrow!

He returns to the stage carrying a sheep.

A fat sheep, I dare say!
A good fleece, dare I lay!

He winks at the audience.

> Return when I may,
> But this will I borrow!

Mak hurries off stage, carrying the sheep.

End of Scene I

Scene II

Mak's cottage is seen, both inside and out. Inside, Gill is sitting at a spinning wheel. Near her is a cot and beside it a cradle. There is a crude table and a chair. Mak creeps up on the outside and knocks at the door. He calls to Gill.

MAK   How, Gill, art thou in? Get us some light.

GILL   *crossly*

> Who makes such a din at this time of the night?
> I am set for to spin. Though I answer, I might
> Not get a penny. A curse on this blight!

She speaks in exasperation to the audience as she rises.

> So fares
> A housewife that has been —
> To be thus put upon!
> Here no work may be done
> For such small cares!

Mak calls out desperately.

MAK   Good wife, open the lock! Sees thou not what I
       bring?

GILL   I beg thee draw the latch.

She goes to the door and opens it. She addresses Mak with mock tenderness.

> Ah, come in, my sweeting!

MAK   Yea, thou need not reck of my long waiting.

Gill sees the sheep in his arm.

GILL   By the naked neck thou art like for to hang!

Mak enters the cottage.

MAK   Go away!
       I am worthy of my meat!
       In straits, I can get
       More than they that swink and sweat
       All the long day.

He holds out the sheep to Gill.

> Thus it fell to my lot, Gill, I had such grace.

Gill shakes her head dubiously.

GILL   It were a foul blot to be hanged for the case.

MAK   I have escaped, Jelott, oft as narrow a place.

GILL   "So long goes the pot to the water," man says,
          "At last
      Comes it home broken."

MAK   Well know I that token.
      But let it never be spoken! —
          Now come and help fast.
      I wish he were slaughtered. I would like to eat;
      This twelvemonth long I have starved for sheep
          meat.

GILL   *anxiously*
      If they come ere he's slain, and hear the sheep
          bleat — ?

MAK   Then might I be taken. That would be a cold sweat!

He pauses and faces Gill.

      Go bar
      The cottage door.

GILL   Yes, Mak.

She closes the door.

      For if they come at thy back —

MAK   Then might I fare, at the hands of the pack,
          The worse by far.

They look about the room for a place to hide the sheep. Then Gill has a sudden inspiration.

GILL   A good jest have I spied, since you know none.
      Here the sheep we shall hide, until they be gone,
      In my cradle.

Mak rushes up to embrace her. She pushes him off.

> Abide. Let me alone! —
> And I'll lie beside him in childbed and groan.

Mak falls in with the plan delightedly.

MAK   Well said!
     And I'll say thou hast brought
     Forth a boy child this night!

GILL   Now is the day bright
       That ever I was bred!

     This is a good trick, and a fair cast.
     A woman's advice helps at the last.

She pauses and grows thoughtful.

     We never know who's spying. Go back again fast.

Mak nods his head in agreement. He puts the sheep in the cradle.

MAK   I'll return ere they rise. Else blows a cold blast!
      I shall go sleep.

He hugs Gill and leaves the cottage. He pauses outside and speaks to the audience.

     Still sleeps all this company.
     I shall go privily,
     As if it were never I
      That carried off their sheep.

He runs off stage.

End of Scene II

Scene III

The moors near Horbury. Mak and the three shepherds are lying on the ground asleep, just as they settled themselves in Scene I.

Mak is snoring loudly between Gib and Daw. Slowly Coll wakes up, stretches and tries to rise.

COLL   *Resurrex a mortuis!* Have hold of my hand!

No one grasps his hand. He looks about, then heaves himself to his feet.

> *Judas Carnas dominus!* I can hardly stand!
> My foot is asleep. My mouth's full of sand!
> I thought we had laid us down near England.

Gib sits up and rubs his eyes.

GIB   Ah, yea!
> But I have slept well!

He lumbers to his feet.

> As fresh as an eel,
> As light I feel
>   As a leaf on a tree!

Daw gets up in a daze. He speaks to no one in particular, not noticing his companions.

DAW   *Benedicite* herein! See my body quake!
> My heart is out of my skin, so hard doth it make!
> Who's making this din? My brow is so black
> To the door will I win.

He staggers about looking for a door, then realizes where he is and pauses. He sees the others, then cries out in alarm.

>   Hark, fellows, wake!
>   We were four!
> See ye aught of Mak now?

Coll pats him on the shoulder and points to Mak asleep on the ground.

COLL   We were up ere thou.

GIB   Man, I here avow
         That he went nowhere.

Daw has a hard time waking up and shaking off his dream.

DAW   Me thought he was wrapped in a wolf-skin.

COLL   So are many now lapped, namely within.

DAW   When we had long napped, I thought — with a gin
     A fat sheep he trapped. But he made no din.

GIB   Be still.
     Thy dream makes thee mad.
     'Tis but phantom, not deed.

COLL   Now God turn all to good,
         If it be His will!

Gib shakes Mak.

GIB   Now, rise, Mak. For shame! Thou lies right long!

Mak pretends to awaken slowly. He sits up stiffly.

MAK   Now, God save us all and send us His love!
     What is this? By Saint James, I can barely move!

He feels himself all over.

         I think I'm the same. Ah, my neck is as stiff
           As a stump.

Coll and Gib help to pull him to his feet.

         Mickle thanks!

He staggers about a little, then shows his fright at the dream he has had.

Since yester even,
Now, by Saint Stephen,
I was flayed with a vision
That made my heart jump.

I thought Gill began to croak and labor full sad,
Well near at the first cock, with a young lad
To add to our flock. Were this true, I'm not glad.
I'd have more to attend to than ever I had.

He winces.

Ah, my head!
A house full of sprouts!
The devil knock them out.
Woe to him has many mouths
And little bread!

He pauses, then takes his leave of the shepherds, offering to let them search him.

I must go home, by your leave, to Gill, as I thought.
I pray you, look up my sleeve, that I steal nought.
I am loath you to grieve, or from you take aught.

He makes a mock bow and runs off stage. Daw calls after him.

DAW   Go forth! Ill may you fare!

To the others.

Now would I we sought
This morn
That we have all our store.

COLL   I will go before.
Let us meet.

GIB   Where?

DAW   At the crooked thorn.

Coll goes off in one direction, Gib in the other. Daw follows Gib.

End of Scene III

Scene IV

The scene is Mak's cottage. Gill is spinning. Mak runs for the door in agitation. He knocks softly and calls out in a hoarse whisper.

MAK   Undo this door! Who is here? How long must I
             wait?

Gill looks up, but does not get up immediately.

GILL   Who makes such a din? Now, walk in at the gate!

MAK   Ah, Gill, what cheer? It is I, Mak, your mate.

Gill rises and goes to the door, grumbling.

GILL   Then may we see the Devil caught in a bit.
             Sir Gill!

She makes fun of Mak's whispering.

             Lo, he comes with a croak,
             As he were held by the neck.
             I can't sit at my work
             Even a little while!

She opens the door. Mak enters hastily and reproaches Gill.

MAK   Will ye hear how she fusses and makes an excuse,
             While she does naught but dawdle and loll at her
             ease?

Gill turns on him angrily.

GILL   Why, who wanders? Who wakes? Who comes?
Who goes?
Who brews? Who bakes? What makes me thus
hoarse?
And then
'Tis pity to behold,
Now in hot, now in cold,
Full sad the household
That lacks a woman!

Gill pauses and lowers her voice.

But what end hast thou made with the herdsman,
Mak?

MAK   The last word that they said when I turned my back,
They would look that they had all their sheep in the
pack.
I doubt not they'll grieve, when they their sheep
lack,
Perdee!

He shrugs his shoulders.

Howe'er the game comes out,
'Tis me they will doubt,
And make a great shout,
And cry out against me.

But do as thou promised.

GILL   We'll do as I said.
I'll swaddle him here in the cradle beside.

She starts to wrap the sheep in a cloth.

     If 'twere a worse pinch, yet help thee, I could.

She places the "baby" in the cradle and lies down on the cot.

     I shall lie down straightway. Come, cover the bed.

MAK   I will.

He picks up a blanket and puts it over her. She shows him where to tuck it in.

GILL   Behind!

Mak finishes tucking her in and stands aside.

     Come Coll and his marrow,
     They will nip us full narrow.

Mak is looking more worried than ever.

MAK   But I may call out "Halloo!"
      The sheep if they find.

Gill sits up to give him his final instructions.

GILL   Listen well when they call. They will come soon.
     Now, come, make ready all; then go sing alone.
     Sing "Lullay" thou shall, for I must groan
     And cry out a-moaning on Mary and John
      For sore.
     Sing thee "Lullay" on fast,
     When thou hears them at last.

> If I play a false cast,
> > Trust me no more!

She lies down and settles the blanket around her. Mak sits down miserably near the door.

End of Scene IV

Scene V

The moors near Horbury. Coll enters from the side of the stage, looking very glum. Gib and Daw enter from the opposite side and greet him.

DAW   Ah, Coll, good morn. Why art thou so black?

COLL   Alas, that ever was I born! We have had bad luck!
      A fat wether have we lost!

DAW   Marry, from our flock?

GIB   Who should show us such scorn? That is a foul trick!

COLL   Some shrew!
    I have sought with my dogs
    All Horbury shrogs,
    And of fifteen young hogs,
      Found I all but one ewe.

Daw looks grim.

DAW   Believe me, if ye will. By St. Thomas of Kent,
      Either Mak or his Gill were in on that accident!

Coll disagrees.

COLL   Peace, Man, be still! I saw when he went.
      Thou slanders him ill. Thou ought to repent
        With speed.

Gib agrees with Daw.

GIB   Now, as ever prosper I,
            Though I should ever here die,
            I would say it were he
                That did that same deed!

DAW   Go we thither, I counsel, and run on our feet.

He raises his right hand, taking an oath.

            I shall never eat bread till the truth I can state!

Coll holds up his hand.

COLL   Nor shall I take a drink in my head till we meet!

Gib holds up his hand.

GIB   I'll not rest for a moment until I him greet,
            My brothers.
            One promise I'll state —
            Till I have him in sight,
            I'll never sleep one night
                Where I did another!

They all shake hands, then stalk off stage to find Mak.

End of Scene V

Scene VI

Mak's cottage. Within, Mak is sitting by the door, nervously listening for noises outside and singing a lullaby. Gill is lying on the cot, groaning. The three shepherds come on stage and pause outside to listen.

DAW   Will ye hear how they hack? Our sire likes to croon.

COLL   Heard I never none croak so far out of tune.
       Call to him.

Gib steps up to the door and knocks.

GIB   Mak, undo your door soon!

Mak jumps up and looks with anguish at Gill. She groans louder than ever and motions to him to answer the knock. He croaks his response without opening the door.

MAK   Who is it that spake, as if it were noon
          Aloft?
       Who is that, I say?

Daw raps loudly on the door and turns to his companions.

DAW   Good fellows, were it day —

Mak interrupts, pretending to beg for quiet.

MAK   As far as ye may,
          Good sirs, speak soft!

       Of a sick woman take heed, that is in malaise.
       I would rather be dead than she had a disease.

Gill groans more loudly than ever, and calls out to the visitors.

GILL   Go elsewhere instead! — I can hardly wheeze! —
       Each footstep ye tread hits the balls of my eyes
          So hard.

Coll knocks at the door impatiently.

COLL   Tell us, Mak, if ye may,
           How fare ye, I say?

Mak opens the door and pretends to be surprised to see them.

MAK   But ye are here today?
           Now, how have ye fared?

He beckons them to come in and tries to be hospitable.

           Ye have run in the mire, and are still wet!
           I'll make ye a fire, if ye will but sit. —
           A nurse would I hire — Know ye one yet? —

He points to the cradle.

           Well spent is my hire — My dream, this is it! —
             For a season!
           I have bairns, if ye knew,
           Well more than enow.
           But we must drink as we brew,
             And that is but reason.

He flutters about them, offering them chairs, looking for food to offer them, etc.

           I would ye dined ere ye went. Methink that ye
             sweat.

The shepherds are unmoved by his friendly gestures and stand looking at him threateningly.

GIB   Nay, neither mends our temper — drink nor meat.

MAK   Why, sirs, ails you aught?

DAW   Yea, the sheep that we get
           Are stolen as they wander. Our loss is great!

Mak offers a tray of tankards, which the shepherds decline.

MAK   Sirs, a drink!

Daw's statement begins to sink in. Mak bristles with mock sympathy and indignation at their loss.

> Had I only been there
> Someone would have bought it full dear!

COLL   Marry, some men believe that ye were,
>   And that gives us to think.

GIB   Mak, some men believe that it was ye.

DAW   Either you or your spouse, so say we.

Mak looks horrified and protests his innocence.

MAK   Now, if you suspect either Gill or me,

He makes a sweeping gesture inviting them to search his cottage.

> Come, rip up our house, — and then ye may see
>   The better
> If I took any ewe,
> Any steer or cow!

He points sadly at the cot.

> And Gill has been low,
>   Here since she laid her.

> As I am true and loyal, to God here I pray
> That this is the first meal I shall eat this day.

Gib and Daw start to search.

COLL   Mak, as I may have bliss, take counsel, I say!
>   "He learned early to steal that could not say nay."

Coll joins the search. He comes too close to the cradle, and Gill shrieks.

GILL   I wilt!
              Out, thieves! Get thee gone!
              Ye would rob us anon!

Mak reproaches them.

MAK   Hear ye her groan?
              Your hearts should melt!

Coll suspiciously steps even closer to the cradle. Mak hastily tries to pull him aside. Gill screams.

GILL   Away, thieves, from my babe! Come him not near!

MAK   If ye knew how she suffered, your hearts would be
                    sore.
              Ye do wrong, I warn ye, that thus come before
              A woman that's in pain. — But I say no more.

Coll tries to peek into the cradle.

GILL   Ah, my middle!

              I pray to God so mild,
              If ever I you beguiled,
              That I shall *eat* the child
                That lies in this cradle!

Mak hurriedly pushes Coll aside and leans over to comfort Gill. Coll appears to be satisfied and steps away.

MAK   Peace, woman! Ease thy pain, and cry not so!
              Thou spills out thy brain, and makes me full woe,

Gib and Daw give up their search. The three shepherds look at each other.

GIB   I trow our sheep is slain. What find ye two?

DAW   All our work is in vain. We may as well go.

He picks up some ragged clothing from a chair.

> Beside these tatters,
> I can find no flesh,
> Hard nor nesh,
> Salt nor fresh,
>   But two empty platters!

He points to the baby in the cradle, teasing Mak.

> Live cattle but this, tame or wild,
> None, as I have bliss, smell as loud as he smelled!

The shepherds laugh, and Gill sits up indignantly.

GILL   No! As God may ye bless, give me joy of my child!

COLL   We have marked amiss. I hold us beguiled.

GIB   Sir, done!

He turns to Mak politely, as the others start to the door.

> Sire — Our Lady him save! —
> Is your child a knave?

MAK   Any lord might him have,
>   This child, for his son!

Gib offers his hand in friendship, but Mak pretends to be offended and refuses to take it.

GIB   Mak, friends will we be, for we are all one.

MAK   We? Now I hold for me, for amends get I none!
> Farewell all three! I'd be glad were ye gone!

The shepherds shake their heads and leave the cottage. Mak hurries after them, as Gill leaps out of bed. The two of them embrace

and congratulate themselves. Meanwhile, the shepherds pause out-
side.

DAW   "Fair words there may be, but love is there none,"
           This year.

Coll starts to go off stage, then turns and speaks to Gib.

COLL   Gave ye the child anything?

GIB   I trow not one farthing!

DAW   Back again I will fling.
           Await me here.

Daw hurries back to the cottage. Mak and Gill stop and listen.
Gill pops herself back into her bed, and Mak runs to the door, just
as Daw bursts in.

           Mak, take it to no grief if I come to thy bairn.

MAK   Nay! Thou hast done me harm, and ill hast thou
           sworn.

DAW   It will not grieve the child, that little star of morn!
           Mak, with your leave, let me give to your bairn
               But sixpence.

Daw approaches the cradle, while Mak dances about, trying to keep
him away.

MAK   Nay! Go away! He sleeps!

DAW   I think he peeps.

MAK   When he awakens, he weeps!
           I pray you, go hence!

Coll and Gib enter the house.

DAW   Give me leave to kiss him and lift up the clout!

He lifts up the blanket and sees the sheep.

> What the devil is this? He has a long snout!

Coll stands impatiently at the door and motions to Daw to come along.

COLL   He is marked amiss! We wait ill about.

Gib approaches the cradle and nudges Daw aside. He looks in.

GIB   "Ill-spun weft, I wiss, ever comes ill out."
> Aye, so!

He rips off the blanket.

> He is like to our sheep!

Daw cranes his neck.

DAW   How, Gib, may I peep?

Coll comes over and looks in.

COLL   I say, "Nature will creep,
> Where it may not go!"

Gib turns angrily to Mak.

GIB   This was a quaint gaud and a fair cast.
> It was a high fraud!

DAW   Ay, sirs, it wast!

Daw turns to Gill.

> Let's burn this bawd, and bind her fast.
> "A false scold hangs at the last."
> So shalt thou.

He turns in disgust to his friends.

> Will ye see how they swaddle
> His four feet in the middle?

Saw I never in a cradle
A horned lad ere now.

MAK   Peace, I bid thee! Let be your fare!
I am his father, and yon woman him bare.

COLL   What is his name, Mak? — Lo, look at Mak's heir!

Gib takes Mak by the collar and threatens to strike him. The shepherds are really angry now.

GIB   Let be all that! Now, rascal, take care,
I say!

Gill tries to distract them. She leans over and coos into the cradle.

GILL   A pretty child is he
As sits on any woman's knee!
A dillydown, perdee,
To make a man gay!

Daw picks up the sheep and points to his ear.

DAW   I know him by his earmark. That is a good notch!

MAK   I beg you, sirs, listen! His nose has a breach!
             A clerk has since told me he was charmed by a witch!

Coll threatens to strike Mak. Gib has him by one arm, Coll by the other, as Mak falls to his knees in terror.

COLL   This is a false work! I would punish the wretch!
             Get a weapon!

Gill jumps halfway up, blubbering and whining.

GILL   He was taken by an elf!
             I saw it myself!
             When the clock struck twelve,
               Was he misshapen!

GIB   Ye two are indeed two birds of one breed!

COLL   Since they maintain their theft, they should both
             be dead!

Coll starts to pull a knife from his belt. Mak sobs in terror.

MAK   If ever I trespassed, you may cut off my head!
             I'm thrown on your mercy.

Daw, carrying the sheep, steps up to Coll and Gib.

DAW   Sirs, let me be your guide.
             For his guilt
          We should not curse nor thrash,
          Trounce nor lash,
          But have done in a flash,
             And toss him in a quilt.

The two shepherds pause, then shake their heads in agreement. Coll lets go of Mak's arm, while Gib pushes him out the door. Daw puts down the sheep, rips the blanket off Gill's cot, and, with Coll, runs outside and spreads the blanket on the ground. The three shepherds toss Mak two or three times, while Gill stands in the doorway, wringing her hands and crying. They finally dump him on the ground, Daw picks up the sheep, and they leave, while Gill tries to comfort her husband.

End of Scene VI

Scene VII

The scene is a field on a hillside near Bethlehem of Judea. Coll, Gib and Daw trudge wearily on stage.

COLL   Oh, but I'm sore, almost ready to burst!
In faith, I can walk no more. Therefore will I rest!

He sits down heavily. Gib is still grumbling about the theft of his sheep.

GIB   Like a sheep of seven score, he weighed in my fist.

He also stretches wearily.

To sleep anywhere, I think that I list.

DAW   Now I pray you,
Lie ye down here.

COLL   Still these thieves I deplore.

DAW   But why should ye care?
               Now do as I say you.

*They all sit down to rest, and make ready to stretch out for a nap.
An Angel appears in the High Place and sings* Gloria in Excelsis.
*The shepherds rise to their knees, and remain kneeling as the An-
gel addresses them.*

ANGEL   Rise, herdsmen gentle, for now is He born
           That shall take from the Fiend that which Adam
               had lorn.
           The Devil to destroy, this night is He born.
           God is made your friend now at this morn,
               He attests.
           To Bethlehem go see!
           There lies that Baby
           In a crib full poorly
               Betwixt two beasts.

*The Angel disappears, and the shepherds stumble to their feet,
as if in a daze.*

COLL   This was as strange a voice as ever yet I heard.
           It is a marvel to name, thus to be afeared.

GIB   Of God's Son of Heaven, he spake a word.

> In a lightning, methought, all the wood appeared
> So fair.

DAW   He spoke of a Bairn
> In Bethlehem, I you warn.

Coll points to the sky. The others follow his gaze.

COLL   So betokens yon star!
> Let us seek Him there!

They start to move toward the direction of the star, but pause.

GIB   Say, what was his song? Heard ye not how it rang,
> Three breves to a long?

DAW   Yea, so well he sang,
> There was no crotchet missing, nor anything wrong.

COLL   Just as he chanted, for to sing us along,
> I can.

Gib and Daw look at him scornfully.

GIB   Let's see how ye croon.
> Can ye bark at the moon?

DAW   Hold your tongue! Have done!

Coll appears to be oblivious of their disapproval.

COLL   Hark after, then!

Coll clears his throat, but Gib interrupts, speaking very seriously.

GIB   We find by prophecy —

To Daw

>   Let be your din! —

> Of David and Isaiah, and more than I mind,
> 'Twas foretold by clergy, that in a Virgin
> Should he light and lie, to free us from sin

And slake it,
And save mankind from woe.
For Isaiah said so:
"*Ecce virgo*
    Concipiet a child that is naked."

DAW Full glad may we be and await this day,
This Lovely One to see, Who all things may.
Oh, Lord, it were well with me, for once and for aye,
Might I kneel on my knee, some word for to say
    To that Child.
But the Angel said
In a crib was He laid.
He was poorly arrayed,
    Both mean and mild.

COLL Patriarchs that have been, and prophets before,
They desired to see this Child that is born.
They are gone full clean. This sight they have lorn.
We shall see him, I ween, ere it be morn,
    As token!
When I see Him, and feel,
I'll know full well
It is as true as steel
    What prophets have spoken:

That to men as poor as we, He would appear,
Find us first, and declare Himself through His
        messenger!

GIB Go we now! Let us fare! The place is us near.

DAW I am ready, and more. Go we together
    To that Light.

He prays.

> Lord, if Thy will be —
> We are simple, all three —
> Thou doth grant joy
>   To comfort Thy wight!

The shepherds follow the star.

End of Scene VII

Scene VIII

A stable in Bethlehem. Mary is seated beside the manger, holding the Christ Child in her arms. Coll, Gib and Daw enter slowly and kneel at a distance from the vision. Coll is the first to approach the Virgin. He kneels at her feet.

COLL   Hail, Comely and Clean! Hail, young Child!
            Hail Maker, as I mean, from a Maiden so mild!
            Thou hast vanquished, I ween, the Warlock so wild;
            The Beguiler of men, now is he beguiled.

Coll looks up at the Baby, then turns briefly to his friends.

Lo, He merries!
Lo, He laughs! My Sweeting!
This is a fair meeting!
I have brought Thee a greeting.
Have a bob of cherries!

He holds up the cherries, to dangle them before the Baby for a moment, then lays them at Mary's feet. He retires and kneels at the edge of the stage, as Gib comes forward and kneels before Mary.

GIB   Hail, sovereign Saviour! For Thou hast us bought!
Hail, noble Flower, That all things hast wrought!
Hail, Full of Favor, That made all of nought!
Hail! I kneel and I cower! A bird have I brought
    To my Fair.

He holds out a bird, then places it at Mary's feet.

Hail, little tiny Mop!
Of our Creed, Thou art the Crop!
I would drink of Thy cup,
    Little Day Star!

Gib falls back and kneels at a distance, as Daw approaches the Virgin.

DAW   Hail, Darling Dear, Full of Godhead!
I pray Thee be near when that I have need.
Hail! Sweet is Thy cheer! My heart doth bleed
To see Thee sit here in such poor weed,
    With no pennies.
Hail! Put forth Thy dall!
I bring Thee but a ball.
Have and play Thee withal
    At the tennis.

He offers the ball to the Baby, then places it at Mary's feet and retires to kneel beside Gib.

MARY The Father of Heaven, God Omnipotent,
      That made all in seven, His Son has He sent.
      My name did He name and light ere He went.
      I conceived this Child through His might, as He
          meant,
        And now is He born.
      May He keep you from woe!
      I shall pray Him do so.
      Speak forth as ye go,
        And think on this morn.

Coll rises from his knees and bows to the Virgin.

COLL Farewell, Lady, so fair to behold,
      With Thy Child on Thy knee!

Gib rises and makes his obeisance.

GIB   But He lies full cold!
      Lord, well is me! Now we go, Thou behold!

Daw rises and stands in his place, as if struck with wonder.

DAW Forsooth, already It seems to be told
        Full oft!

COLL What Grace we have found!

Gib crosses over to Coll, and the two start off stage.

GIB Come forth! Now are we won!

DAW To sing are we bound.
      Let us praise Him aloft!

He bows to the Virgin, and follows the others off stage.

Curtain

Herod *and* the Magi

From the play of THE MAGI, HEROD, and THE SLAUGHTER OF THE INNOCENTS, *as acted by the Shearmen and Taylors of Coventry*

CAST *of* CHARACTERS

ANNOUNCER	*Attendants to the Three Kings*
KING HEROD	MARY
A HERALD	JOSEPH
HEROD'S COURTIERS	AN ANGEL
FIRST KING, *Jaspar of Taurus*	
SECOND KING, *Balthasar of Araby*	
THIRD KING, *Melchior of Aginare*	

Prologue

Enter an Announcer, richly dressed and very pompous. Behind him come Herod and the Herald, with other Courtiers. The Announcer steps to the center of the very front of the stage. Herod stands haughtily alone to one side, slightly behind him. The Herald stands opposite Herod. The Courtiers range themselves in a semicircle between. The Announcer motions to the audience for silence, and speaks directly to it.

ANNOUNCER

> Peace! Peace, my lords and barons of great renown!
> Peace, seigneurs, chevaliers, and gentlemen!
> And, peace, I say, companions great and small!
> I order you: Keep silence, one and all!
> Peace! For your noble king is present here!

He turns and bows deeply to King Herod.

> Let no one in this company dare cheer
> Nor clap nor hiss nor hoot. But hold your tongues!
> Show the respect that to your sire belongs.
> For he's your king, your lord, all-powerful.
> In his name, cease your chatter, I bespeak you,
> For he's great Herod!

He bows again to Herod, then turns briefly to the audience.

> Now, may the Devil take you!

The Announcer leaves the stage.

Scene I

The Court of King Herod. Herod steps forward and monopolizes the front of the stage, striding up and down, as he speaks directly to the audience. The Herald and the Courtiers stand in the background.

HEROD Herod am I, the king
   Of Judah and Israel,
  And the mightiest conqueror
   That ever walked on the ground!
  For I am even he
   That made both Heaven and Hell,
  And of my own great power
   I hold the whole world bound.
  Magog and other princes,
   All these I did confound;

He whips his sword from its sheath and brandishes it before the audience.

  And with this shining brand,
   Their bones I broke asunder,
  Till all the watching world
   At Herod's blows did wonder.

He pauses and glares fiercely at the audience.

  I, Herod, am the cause
   Of lightning and of thunder.
  It is through my fury
   That they such noise do make.
  My fearful countenance
   The clouds doth so encumber
  That oftentimes for dread of me
   The very earth doth shake!
  Look! When I with malice
   This bright sword do shake,
  All men on this earth living,

From North even to South,
I can destroy them all,
    With one word from my mouth!

He pauses again. He becomes slightly less fierce, but remains
arrogant.

To make you an accounting
    Of all my wealth immense,
That would be too much
    For any tongue to tell!
The whole vast Orient
    Owes me obedience.
I'm Prince of Purgatory,
    And Chief Captain of Hell!
And all Hell's traitorous devils
    By force can I compel
Mine enemies to vanquish
    And down to dust them drive.

With just a twink of my eye,
Not one will be left alive!

He gives the audience an exaggerated wink, snaps his fingers, and laughs horribly. Then he changes his tone to one of self-admiration. He touches himself lightly as he describes his beauty.

Behold my handsome face,
My brilliant coloration,
Brighter than the sun
At noontide of the day!
Where could you ever find
A greater satisfaction
Than to behold my person
Which is so very gay?
My falcon! And my falchion!
My whole gorgeous array!
He that hath the good fortune
Always on me to blink,
Why, he can live forever
Without other meat or drink!

He turns and beckons to his Herald, who comes forward and bows respectfully.

Therefore, my good herald,
Who art called Calcace,
In every port declare it:
That no ships may arrive,
Nor any alien strangers
Through my realm may pass,
Unless they for their passage-fee
Do pay me gold marks five.
Now, speed thee forth hastily.

All those that will be contrary,
    Upon a gallows hanged shall be.
And, by Mahomet, they shall see
    From me they'll get no grace!

HERALD   Now, lord and master, in all haste
    Thy worthy wishes shall be wrought,
Thy word be spread, thy country crossed
    As swiftly as it can be thought.

The Herald bows and departs, running. Herod turns again to the audience.

HEROD   Now shall our realm throughout be sought
    In every place, both East and West.
If any villains to me are brought,
    They shall find nothing to their taste.

He chuckles. Then he yawns and motions to his Courtiers.

And while I take my royal rest,
    Trumpets and viols and other harmony
Shall sooth the wakefulness of my majesty!

He walks languidly off stage, followed by his courtiers.

End of Scene I

Scene II

A countryside near Jerusalem. Enter the First King, Jaspar of Taurus, with his attendants. He sees a star shining in the distance.

FIRST KING

Now blessed be God, for His sweet care!
    For yonder a bright star I see!
Now is He come to us from far,

As the prophet said that it should be.

He said a Babe there should be born,
From the root of Jesse's tree,
To save mankind that was forlorn.
Now truly come to us is He.

Reverence to Him will I do,
As God That hath made all from nought.
All prophets said that it is so:
With His blood mankind shall be bought.

May He grant me grace,
By yon star I see,
And into that place
May He now bring me,
That I may worship Him humbly
And see His glorious face.

The First King and his attendants move to the back of the stage.
From the opposite side enter the Second King, Balthasar of Araby,
and his attendants.

SECOND KING

Lost from my way, I think I am,
For signs of this land, none can I see!
Now, God, That on this earth made man,
Send me some knowledge of where I may be.

Yonder, methink, a star I see,
Which signifies the birth of a Child,
That hither is come to make man free.
He is born of a Maiden, undefiled.

To worship that Child is mine intent.
Further now will I take my way.

He sees the First King.

> I trust God hath me some company sent,
> > For yonder a king travels on his way.
>
> Toward him now will I ride.

He approaches the First King.

> Hail, comely king, I do you pray,
> Unto what coast you go this tide,
> > Or whither indeed lies your journey?

The First King comes forward to greet the Second.

FIRST KING

> To seek a Child is mine intent,
> > Of whom the prophecies have spoken.
> The time is come. Now is He sent.
> > In yonder star you see His token.

SECOND KING

> Sir, I beg you, with your license,
> I'd ride with you into His presence.
> To Him will I offer frankincense,
> > For Head of the Church He shall be.

The two Kings retire backstage as the Third King enters with his attendants.

THIRD KING

> I ride wandering far and wide,
> > Over hills and dales. I know not where I am.
> Now, King of Kings, send me some guide,
> > That I may learn this country's name.
>
> Ah! Yonder I see a vision fair
> > Which means some miracle, I trow.

A Child appearing in a star!
He is come to save us now from woe.

He spies the other two Kings.

Two kings also yonder I see.
To them now will I ride,
For to have their company.
I trust they will me abide.

He turns toward the two Kings, who come forward to meet him.

Hail, comely kings and gently-born,
Whither are ye bound this morn?

FIRST KING

To seek a Child is our intent,
Guided by yon star which ye see.

SECOND KING

For Him I purpose this present.

THIRD KING

Sirs, I pray with humility,
That I may ride in your company.

The three Kings bow to one another, then turn and speak in unison.

THREE KINGS
>To God Almighty now we pray
>That His precious person we may see.

They leave the stage, followed by their attendants.

End of Scene II

Scene III

Herod's Court. Herod enters from one side, followed by his Courtiers. The Herald enters from the opposite side and kneels before his king.

HERALD   Hail, lord! Most mighty one!
>Thy full commandment now is done.
>Into thy land this night are come
>>Three kings with a great company.

Herod is startled. His Courtiers murmur to each other in surprise.

HEROD   What are they doing in my country?

HERALD   They seek a King and a child, they say.

HEROD   Of what age should this young Child be?

HERALD   But scant twelve days in full is He.

Herod is both perplexed and angry.

HEROD   And was He indeed so lately born?

HERALD   Ay, sire, so I was told this morn.

Herod walks about the stage briefly, considering the matter. Then he turns to the Herald, and speaks firmly.

HEROD   Now, in pain of death, bring them unto me!
Therefore, Herald hie thee fast,
    As speedily as thou canst run,
Lest these kings out of my realm have passed.
    And bring them all before my throne!

Herod speaks craftily to the Herald.

    And in Jerusalem seek to learn of the Child.
    But I warn thee, let thy words be mild.
    In this, much subtlety must thou wield,
    That His power be cut — and those kings beguiled!

HERALD   Sire, I am ready at your bidding,
To serve thee as my lord and king.
For joy thereof, see how I spring
With light heart and fresh gamboling
    On this green mold.

The Herald dances a jig.

HEROD   Then speed thee forth hastily,
And see thou bear thee sensibly.
Also, I beg thee heartily,
That thou commend me properly
    Both to young and old!

The Herald makes a final bow and leaves the stage. Herod chuckles to himself, then leaves the stage, followed by the Courtiers.

End of Scene III

Scene IV

A roadside near Jerusalem. Enter the Three Kings and their attendants. From the opposite side of the stage enters the Herald.

HERALD   Hail, sir kings of high degree!
      Herod, the lord of these countries wide,
      Desires to speak with you all three,
        And for your coming doth abide.

FIRST KING
      Sir, we are ready to do his will.

He turns to his companions.

      Let us hasten to this king's place.
      To speak with him would please us all.
        That Child we seek, may He grant us grace!

The Three Kings bow to the Herald and follow him off stage.

End of Scene IV

Scene V

Herod's Court. From one side enter Herod and his Courtiers. From the opposite side enter the Herald and the Three Kings. The Herald kneels before Herod.

HERALD   Hail, lord without peer! To thee hither
      These three kings now I have brought.

He rises and retires. Herod steps forward and bows to the Kings, who return his greeting.

HEROD   Now, welcome, sir kings, all together.

He simpers a bit and makes a deprecating gesture.

        But of my brilliance, sirs, fear ye nought!

He becomes more serious.

      Sir kings, it is thus I understand:
      A star hath guided you to my land,
      Wherein great heartening ye find,
         By reason of its splendor bright.
      Wherefore, I pray you heartily
      The truth that you will certify, —
      How long it has been, verily,
         Since of that star you had first sight.

FIRST KING
      Sir king, the very truth to say
         And show to you, as it is best,
      This same is even the twelfth day
         Since it appeared to us in the West.

Herod turns and grimaces at his Courtiers, then speaks unctuously to the Kings.

HEROD   Brothers, there is no more to say.
      With all your hearts, keep on your journey,
      And come back to me by this same way,
         That your news I then may know.
      You shall be fêted in this country
      And in great concord feast with me.
      And that Child then I will go to see
         And honor Him also.

SECOND KING

> Sire, your command we shall fulfill,
> And humbly obey ourselves theretill.
> May He that guideth all things at will,
>> Guide us across your land,
> Sir king, that we may pass in peace!

HEROD   *jovially*

>> Yea, but go freely, at your ease!
> Your passport for a hundred days
> You shall have at my command.

Herod turns to one of his Courtiers, who produces an official-looking scroll. With a great bow, Herod presents it to the Second King.

THIRD KING

>> Now, farewell, king of high degree,
>> Humbly of you our leave we take!

The Three Kings bow. Herod is very gracious.

HEROD   Adieu to you, sir kings, all three.
> And while I live, be bold of me.
> There is nothing whatever in my country,
>> But for your own you may it take.

The Three Kings depart. As soon as they are gone, Herod becomes himself, crafty and sly.

> Now these three kings are gone on their way.
>> Very unwisely have they wrought.
> When they come back, they shall die the same day.
>> Thus shall such wretches to death be brought.
>> Such is my will!

He boasts to the audience.

He that against my laws will hold,
Be he king or Caesar never so bold,
Him will I cast into sorrow cold!
Him indeed will I kill!

He chuckles horribly as he leaves the stage, followed by his Courtiers and the Herald.

End of Scene V

Scene VI

The Stable at Bethlehem. The Stable occupies the center backstage. It is lighted to show Mary and Joseph worshiping the Christ Child in His Manger. After a brief pause, the Kings enter downstage. They do not as yet see the Stable, but keep their faces toward the audience.

FIRST KING

Oh, blessed God, much is Thy might!
Where is the star that gave us light?

SECOND KING

Now let us kneel down in His presence
And beseech our Lord of Magnificence
That we may know, through His excellence,
What His will may be.

They kneel in prayer briefly. As they rise, the Third King points to the star in the distance.

THIRD KING

Yonder, brothers, I see the star,
Whereby I know He is not far.
Let us go on, sir kings, therefore
To this poor place.

*As they turn to follow his glance, they see the Stable. They fall
back in amazement, then approach very reverently. The First King
enters the Stable, followed by an attendant who carries a golden
cup. The King kneels before the Manger.*

FIRST KING

Hail, Lord, That all this world hath wrought!
Hail, God and Man together here!
For Thou hast made all things of nought,
Although Thou liest poorly there.

He takes the cup from his attendant who retires.

A cup of gold I have Thee brought,
In token that Thou hast no peer!

*The First King retires to his place outside the Stable and kneels,
worshiping. The Second King enters the Stable, followed by an
attendant bearing a cup, and kneels before the Manger.*

SECOND KING

Hail, Lord of High Magnificence!
In token of Thy priesthood, see
I bring Thee a cup of frankincense,
For such an offering becometh Thee.

*He takes the cup from his attendant, places it before the Manger,
and retires to kneel outside the Stable. The Third King enters and
kneels, followed by his attendant bearing a cup or bowl.*

THIRD KING

> Hail, Thou Lord, long lookèd for.
> I bring Thee myrrh for mortality,
> In token Thou shalt mankind restore
> To life by Thy death upon a tree.

*The Third King places his gift before the Manger, then retires and
kneels.*

MARY   God have mercy, sir kings, for your goodness!
> By the guiding of the Godhead are ye come.
> May my sweet Son reward you for your largesse,
> And His providence speed your journey home!

The Kings withdraw from the Stable.

End of Scene VI

Scene VII

*A countryside between Bethlehem and Jerusalem. The Three
Kings enter with their attendants.*

FIRST KING

> Sir kings, since we have promised this,
> By Herod homeward we must go.

SECOND KING

> Now truly, brother, we can do no less.
> But I am so weary, I know not what to do.

THIRD KING

> Right so am I. I pray you, therefore,
> Let us rest awhile upon this ground.

FIRST KING

>Brother, your saying doth please my ear.
>May the grace of that Child save us all sound!

They lie down on the ground and fall asleep. An Angel enters and stands before them.

ANGEL

>King of Taurus, Sir Jaspar!
>King of Araby, Sir Balthasar!
>Melchior, King of Aginare!
>>To you now am I sent.
>For fear of Herod, go westward home.
>Into your lands, when you do come,
>You shall be welcomed with great renown.
>>The Holy Ghost this warning hath sent.

The Angel departs. When the Angel has gone, the Kings rise in amazement.

FIRST KING

>Awake, sir kings! Brothers, I pray!
>The voice of an angel I heard in my dream.

SECOND KING

> That is full true, as ye do say,
>> For he spoke full plainly to each his name.

THIRD KING

> He bade we should return by the West,
>> Lest Herod should falsely us betray!

FIRST KING

> To do it so, that way is the best.
>> That Child that we sought, may He guide our way!

He turns, as though he were looking back toward Bethlehem.

> Now farewell, Thou fairest Shape so sweet!
>> And thanked be Jesus for His guiding hand,
> That caused us three thus sudden to meet,
>> Who dwell apart, each in a strange land!

He turns to the other Kings.

> That we should here make our presentation,
>> Cleansed so clean, to the Son of the King
> And unto His Mother, for our salvation,
>> Of much great joy now may we sing,
> That we have thus made our oblation.

The Kings prepare to separate. The Second King steps forward and bows to his companions.

SECOND KING

> Now farewell, Sir Jaspar, to you,
>> King of Taurus, of worthy degree!
> Sir Balthasar, also to you I bow.
>> I thank you both for your company
>> That we together have had.
> He That made us to meet on the hill,

I thank Him now, and ever I will.
For now we may go without suffering ill,
    And of our meeting be full glad.

THIRD KING

    Now since we needs must on our journeys go
      For fear of Herod that is so wroth,
Farewell, brother, and brother, also;
    I take my leave here of you both
      This day on foot.
May He that made us to meet on the plain
And offer to Mary and her sweet Son,
Give us His grace in Heaven again
    Together to meet!

The Kings make their final bows to one another, then leave the stage with their attendants, going in separate directions.

Curtain

Saint Nicholas *and the*
Three Scholars

From TRES CLERICI, *a twelfth-century manuscript of the Abbey Saint-Benoit-sur-Loire*

CAST *of* CHARACTERS

FIRST SCHOLAR	AN OLD MAN
SECOND SCHOLAR	AN OLD WOMAN, *his wife*
THIRD SCHOLAR	SAINT NICHOLAS

The scene represents a road or pathway through a forest. At one side of the stage stands a little cottage. Enter three Scholars trudging wearily along the road.

FIRST SCHOLAR

    We three, whom love of learning has brought
    Thus far to travel on foreign ways,

Should look for a lodging for the night
While the sun still spreads its warming rays.

SECOND SCHOLAR

Yea! He holds his horses upon the shore;
Soon they will dive beneath the sea.
We know nought of this land. Therefore,
Shelter we now must seek, all three.

An old man comes out of the cottage across the stage. He putters about his dooryard, as the Scholars spy him and point to him.

THIRD SCHOLAR

Yonder, look you, there appears
A grave old man, soberly dressed.
Perhaps if we offer to him our prayers,
He will receive us and be our host.

The Scholars approach him politely.

FIRST SCHOLAR

Sire, for love of learning we've come
Many a mile to this foreign coast.

SECOND SCHOLAR

> Pray, give us lodging. We're far from home,
> And we would sleep while the night doth last.

OLD MAN

> Now let the Maker of All be your Host!
> I'll give you no hospitality!
> It would bring me only an extra cost,
> And there would be no benefit for me.

The Scholars are taken aback. The Old Man turns away from them discourteously. As the Scholars whisper together, an Old Woman enters from the cottage. They spy her, and after a brief consultation, the First Scholar approaches her and bows.

FIRST SCHOLAR

> Dear lady, you may grant our plea
> For a place to sleep, though you profit none.
> For such kindness and generosity,
> The Lord may bless you and send you a son.

The Old Woman looks at them, as they all bow to her. After a moment's consideration, she turns to her husband and speaks privately to him.

OLD WOMAN

> Dear husband, to give hospitality

To these poor studious young men
Is the least we can do in charity.
It will bring us no loss; it will bring us no gain.

The Old Man thinks it over, then shrugs his shoulders, and answers her.

OLD MAN

Good wife, I'll listen to what you say.
I'm willing to let them stay the night.

He comes forward to the Scholars.

Now, wandering scholars, come here to me!
You may have the lodging that you have sought.

The Scholars show their gratitude and bow deeply. The Old Woman bustles about to make their beds ready. She fetches cushions from inside the cottage and places them in a row in the center of the stage. She retires to the door of the cottage, while the Old Man leads the Scholars to their pallets, then he joins his wife. The Scholars prepare for bed. They remove their heavy purses and place them on the ground behind their pillows. They wrap themselves in their cloaks, lie down with their heads on the cushions, and soon fall asleep. When they are fast asleep, the Old Man and Old Woman tiptoe over to look at them. The Old Man points to the purses.

Just see how fat these purses be!
There is plenty here of silver and gold.
If it were not for the infamy,
We could steal the money that these do hold.

He continues to stare thoughtfully at the purses, while the Old Woman sighs.

OLD WOMAN

> We have borne the burden of poverty,
> Husband, as long as we've drawn breath.
> We might escape our penury,
> If we had but the heart to put them to death.

They look at one another as the idea begins to gain a hold over them. The Old Woman plucks her husband's sleeve and whispers.

> Come! Take your sword out of its sheath!
> You could have great riches to call your own,
> If you'd put these wanderers to death,
> And no one would know what you had done.

After some hesitation, the Old Man takes out his sword. He stabs the sleepers. They pick up the bodies and carry them, one by one, into the cottage. Then they return and fondle the purses. As they are doing this, they catch sight of someone approaching. Quickly they hide the purses in the cottage and assume modest attitudes as they come out. St. Nicholas enters, dressed in the robes of a bishop and carrying a crosier as a staff. He walks wearily.

ST. NICHOLAS

> A traveler, I, weary of my way.
> Surely I can walk no further.

He sees the old couple and bows to them graciously.

> A lodging for the night, I pray
> You give to me, good sire and mother.

The Old Man and Old Woman hesitate. They whisper.

OLD MAN

> Is this man worthy to be our guest?
> Dear wife, I'll do whatever you say.

OLD WOMAN

> You can see that his rank is of the highest.
> He is nobly born. We should let him stay.

The Old Man nods in agreement. He turns to St. Nicholas and bows politely.

OLD MAN

> Weary traveler, draw thee near.
> You seem to be a gentleman.
> If you desire some dinner here,
> Whatever you wish, I shall try to obtain.

St. Nicholas bows to them. He stands to one side, as they bustle about. The Old Man fetches a chair and a table, which he sets up in the center of the stage, just in front of the cushions left by the

Scholars. The Old Woman sets the table with cutlery and several covered dishes. At last all is ready, and they lead the Saint to the table. He sits down and smacks his lips, while they take their places slightly behind him on either side. One by one, he takes the covers off the dishes and replaces them. As he does so, his expression changes from pleasure to disappointment and finally to anger. He turns first to one, then to another of the couple.

ST. NICHOLAS *fiercely*

> I can eat none of these dishes here!
> Good fresh meat is what I crave!

The Old Man recovers slightly from his astonishment and speaks very humbly.

OLD MAN

> I've brought thee the best of our own poor fare.
> Good fresh meat we do not have.

St. Nicholas jumps up furiously, upsetting the table and chair. He picks up his crosier and shakes it at the Old Man.

SAINT NICHOLAS

> Now you have plainly told a lie!
> Too much fresh meat your cupboards hold!
> Fresh meat you have butchered in villainy!
> You've slaughtered three men to gain their gold!

The old people cling to one another in terror at the Saint's last statement. Then the Old Woman falls to her knees before him.

OLD WOMAN

> Have mercy, good sir, and pity us!
> For you must be a saint from God.

The Old Man falls to his knees before the Saint.

OLD MAN

> Although our crime is hideous,
> Christ Himself might pardon our deed.

They kneel before him in anguish, begging for forgiveness. St. Nicholas strides angrily up and down the stage, then turns to them and speaks sternly.

ST. NICHOLAS

>Bring forth the bodies of the slain,
>And in your hearts repent your sin!
>By God's grace, these dead shall rise again.
>With weeping, ye may your pardon win.

The old couple kneel penitently for a moment, then slowly rise to their feet and enter the cottage. As they go, the Saint brusquely moves the table and the chair aside. The old people carry out the body of the First Scholar, and place it on the ground before the Saint, with its head on a cushion. They bring out the other two in the same manner. Then they fetch the purses, and sigh as they place them on the ground. When they have finished, they kneel before their cottage door. St. Nicholas takes his place in the center of the stage, in front of the three "bodies," and prays.

>Oh, God! From Whom all things have come,
>Heaven and earth and air and sea,
>Raise up these men who are lying dumb.

He turns slightly and indicates the Scholars. He pauses. Then he indicates the old couple.

>And hearken to those that cry out to Thee!

There is a moment of silence. St. Nicholas, his head still bent in

prayer, steps to the side of the stage opposite the couple. Then slowly the First Scholar begins to move, as though he were waking from sleep. The others follow him. They stretch, look about them, reach for their purses, and finally rise to their feet. They look at one another in wonder. As they do so, the Old Man and the Old Woman raise their heads and see the miracle. Their expressions change from contrition to great joy. They lift their arms and faces toward the Saint, who stands immobile with his crosier extended in blessing. They rise, and the whole cast bows to the audience and leaves the stage.

Curtain

The Statue *of* Saint Nicholas

From LUDUS SUPER ICONIA SANCTI NICOLAI, *by Hilarius*

CAST *of* CHARACTERS

SAINT NICHOLAS,
  a statue

A *band of robbers*

BARBARUS, *a heathen*
  merchant

The scene opens upon a statue of Saint Nicholas in an open space, either a clearing in a woodland or a deserted village square. St. Nicholas is dressed as a bishop and carries a crosier. Barbarus, a heathen merchant, enters tugging at a heavy chest. He is dressed in a turban and full trousers, to show that he is an infidel. He tugs and pushes at the chest until he finally nudges it into position beside the pedestal of the statue. Then he sits down on his box, wipes his brow, and rests for a moment. While he is resting, robbers slip quietly on stage from either side and tiptoe into positions at the

back, unseen by Barbarus. They hide themselves behind tree trunks,
corners of buildings, folds of the back curtain, or wherever they
may. Barbarus finally rises and addresses the statue.

BARBARUS

> Nicholas, all my earthly goods,
> Silver ducats, broidered hoods,
> In this chest of heavy woods,
>   I have brought to thee.
> All the wealth that I have stored,
> Jeweled scabbard, graven sword,
> Pearls and gold, a goodly hoard,
>   You must keep for me.

He struts about the stage, feeling his importance. He shakes his
finger at St. Nicholas.

Listen well to what I say.
I must travel far away,
For a busy man am I,
    A man of great affairs.
While I travel o'er the land,
You, a saint, must keep your stand.
Therefore, to your guarding hand,
    I commend my cares.

While he is speaking, the robbers peep out from their hiding places and motion to each other, pointing to the treasure and mimicking him. He is unaware of their presence.

Custodian, sir, you now must be
Of all these riches that you see!

Barbarus opens the top of the chest and displays a few of his treasures to the statue, while the robbers try to peek over his shoulder without being noticed. He closes the chest, and speaks in a threatening voice.

When I return, restore to me
    All my possessions, Saint!

Allow no thieves and robbers here
To spoil me of my rightful gear,
Lest when I come, you suffer dear
    And proper punishment!

The robbers look amused and tiptoe off stage. Barbarus takes a whip from his belt and brandishes it before the statue.

Though you may be a saint, or higher,
When I return, you'll feel the fire
Of all my worldly wrath and ire,
    If anything's amiss!

He tucks the whip back into his belt, closes the lock of the chest

and locks it with a large key which he wears on a ring at his belt.
Then he starts toward the exit. He pauses.

Now that I have made known to you
What I propose that you shall do,
With a more carefree heart I go,
  Nicholas, I confess!

Barbarus leaves the stage. One by one the robbers come out of
their hiding places and gather around the chest. They try to pick
the lock, but cannot do so. At last the leader takes a heavy knife
from his belt and pries open the lid. They reach into the chest and

take out treasures, which they show to the audience with much de-
light. For example, one takes out a cloak with gold embroidery,
drapes it over his shoulders and swaggers about the stage while
the others applaud. Another pulls out a "jeweled scabbard" and
flourishes the sword within it. Several pluck out bags of coins
which they jingle. When the chest is empty, they close the lid,
dance around it in glee, then run off stage in different directions.
After they have gone, Barbarus returns. He is swaggering more
proudly than ever, and wears several new money-bags at his waist.
He walks confidently to the chest, takes out his key, and prepares
to open the lock, when he realizes that the lock is broken. He looks
about in dismay, throws open the lid and sees that the chest is
empty, then turns to the audience in anguish.

BARBARUS

    Oh, Fortune, cruel and hard!

He points to the statue.

    With this unworthy guard
    I trusted all my hoard.
       Alas! Oh, Misery!
    Who loses all, a sorry man is he!

He looks into his chest again, to make sure he isn't dreaming.

    A hundred coins and more
    Were in this box before!
    Now, not a penny's here!
       Alas! Oh, Misery!
    Who loses all, a sorry man is he!

He cries loudly.

    My goods are gone! Oh, shame
    And grief! I do proclaim
    The statue is to blame!
       Alas! Oh, Misery!
    Who loses all, a sorry man is he!

He turns to the statue.

> I gave you here in trust
> The wealth within this chest.
> Oh, what a sorry jest!

He shakes his fist.

> Ha, Nicholas!
> Give back my gold or suffer what you must!

He pulls out his whip.

> I've paid to you much honor,
> And now I am the mourner!
> You'll rue your misdemeanor.
>   Ha, Nicholas!
> Return my goods, or have a taste of this!

> I swear it by thy Master!
> If you would shun disaster,
> Restore my gold the faster!
>   Ha, Nicholas!
> Refill my chest, or lose your happiness!

He starts to whip the statue, which slowly comes to life and climbs down from the pedestal. Barbarus puts away his whip, makes a threatening gesture to the Saint, who ignores him, and then Barbarus stomps off the stage.

St. Nicholas makes a search of the rear of the stage and discovers the robbers. One by one, he pulls them out from their hiding places, leads them by the ears into positions in a semicircle and makes them kneel. He addresses them sternly.

ST. NICHOLAS

Oh, wretched men, what have you done?
No longer shall the heavenly sun
   Shine on your evil joy.
For I was watching when you crept
Thieving, robbing here, and slipped
   Silently away.

Now I've had many a thump and whack,
Because I could not render back
   All that I should do.
Curses, bitter words, and more
I've borne, as well as whipping sore.
   Therefore I haste to you.

Give back into the merchant's coffer
All that you have stolen, and offer

Your prayers for grace.
Whatever Barbarus gave to me
In trust, restore immediately
Into its place.

He raises his bishop's crosier threateningly.

If you do not do this thing,
From a gibbet you shall swing
Ere the night fall.
I shall proclaim to judge and city
Your sin and guilt. There'll be no pity
Upon you all.

The robbers plead silently with him, holding up their hands in various attitudes of begging. He nudges them to rise one by one and to take the treasures back to the chest. Each one does so in his turn, then goes back to his place in the semicircle and kneels again in prayer. When they have all completed their chores, St. Nicholas returns to his pedestal and resumes his original position.

Barbarus enters, sees the robbers kneeling, and runs to the chest. When he opens it, he shouts in wonder.

BARBARUS

Unless my eyes deceive,
All is well!
My treasure I receive.
Oh, what a miracle!
The lost is here again!
All is well!
The effort was not mine!
Oh, what a miracle!

He turns enthusiastically to the statue.

What a good guardian!

All is well!
Thou hast returned my own!
Oh, what a miracle!

He kneels before the statue.

Upon my knees to thee
I come, St. Nicholas,
For thou hast kept for me
The treasures I possess.

I've traveled far away,
St. Nicholas, from thee,
But thou restorest today
My earthly property!

The Saint stretches out his arm and speaks slowly to Barbarus, who bows his head.

ST. NICHOLAS

Do not, brother, pray to me.
'Twas not I, but God above,
Maker of heaven and earth and sea,
Who hath shown thee here His love.

Pray to Him, and praise His name.
Only in that God believe

And in Christ, His only Son.
 Any other Gods deceive.

Mend thy ways, and turn to Him.
 Be no more an infidel.
God hath stretched His loving hand
 To thee in this miracle.

Barbarus rises from his knees. The robbers follow his example. He steps forward and addresses the audience.

BARBARUS

 I shall hesitate no more,
 But acknowledge Him today.
 Heathen I have been before.
 From my sins I draw away.

He turns to the statue.

 Since my wealth He hath restored,
 I, too, restoration make
 Of my soul unto my Lord,
 Honored Saint, for Jesus' Sake.

Barbarus takes off his turban, his rich cloak, his belt with the moneybags, sword, etc., and lays them on the chest. The Saint smiles in blessing upon him, then resumes his position as a statue. Barbarus, his head bowed, walks slowly to the exit. As he moves off, the robbers follow him in a single line. Each pauses at the chest and places there his knives, moneybags, cloaks, etc.

Curtain

G L O S S A R Y

In the "dictionary" which follows, you will find the meanings of Latin phrases, as well as of words used in this book which are no longer common in our language. I have omitted certain words which may be unfamiliar to some of you, because these are to be found in modern dictionaries. The Thorndike Century Junior Dictionary, Revised Edition, by E. L. Thorndike, published by Scott, Foresman and Company, has been my reference. *Any word not given below may be found there.*

A number of the expressions used in these plays have come down to the present day with their forms intact, but with their meanings changed. For instance, when we say "annoy," we usually mean "tease," "disturb," or "vex." When the Angel tells Noah that the Lord will "annoy" mankind, he means something much stronger — "punish," "do injury to," or even "destroy." Words like this I have included here. You would have a hard time making sense of them, if you had to depend on modern definitions only.

A

ADREAD, *adj.*: afraid, terrified

ANNOY, *v.*: punish, do injury to, destroy

ARRAYED, *adj.*: ("I hold me well arrayed") ready, prepared

B

BALE, *n.*: trouble, unpleasantness

BAWD, *n.*: a rascally woman

Benedicite! (Latin): God bless us!

BENT, *n.*: ("As I walk on this bent"), a grassy field

BOW, *n.*: ("This bow here between Him and thee"), a rainbow

BRAND, *n.*: a sword

BREACH, *n.*: ("His nose has a breach"), a slit, a break

BREVES, *n.*: short notes in music

C

CAST, *n.*: ("a fair cast") a trick

CHEER, *n.*: ("She has a sour cheer," or "Why do you make this heavy cheer?") face, facial expression

CHEVALIERS, *n.*: members of a certain order of knighthood

COMPANIONS, *n.*: members of a low order of knighthood

D

DALL, *n.*: hand, fist

DIN, *n.*: fuss, racket

Dominus! (Latin): Lord!

E

Ecce Virgo concipiet (Latin): Behold! A Virgin shall conceive

EEN, *n.*: eyes

ENOW, *adj.* or *adv.*: enough

F

FARE, *n.*: ("Let be your fare") noise, racket

FORLORN, *adj.*: lost

G

GAUD, *n.*: trick, joke

GEAR, *n.*: equipment, property, belongings

GIN, *n.*: net, trap

GLOSS, *n.*: ("Thou hast an ill gloss") shine, reputation

GOSSIPS, *n.*: close friends, especially women

GRILL, *v.*: cause discomfort or distress

H

HACK, *v.*: croak, sing out of tune

HIGHT, *n.*: height ("On hight" means "on high.")

HIND, *n.*: ("Thou art a sorry hind") fellow

HIND, *n.*: ("hart and hind") a female deer

HOGS, *n.*: young sheep

I

In Excelsis Gloria! (Latin): Glory to God in the highest!

IWISS, or I-WISS, *adv.* or *interj.*: indeed, certainly

J

Judas Carnas Dominus! (Latin): a profane exclamation

K

KNAVE, *n.*: boy

L

LAUDS, *n.*: ("When they rang Lauds") ringing of church bells to indicate the first hour of the day

LIEFER, *adv.*: rather

LIST, *n.* or *v.*: desire, wish

LORN, *adj.*: lost

M

MAGOG, *n.*: a legendary prince who led an army for Satan

MAIN, *n.*: ("With topgallant and jib and main") mainsail

MAIN, *n.*: ("with all our main") strength, power

MALAISE, *n.*: illness, distress

Manus tuas commendo, Pontio Pilato! (Latin): "Into your hands I commend myself, Pontius Pilate!", a mocking prayer. Mak is pretending to be pious, but he cannot help showing what a rascal he really is.

MARK, *n.*: a medieval coin, unit of money

MARROW, *n.*: ("Come Coll and his marrow") company

MEAN, *n.*: ("Then the mean falls to me") the middle part in music, the alto

MERRIES, *v.*: ("Lo: He merries!") smiles, laughs

MOLD, *n.*: earth, ground

N

NESH, *adj.*: soft

P

PALFREY, *n.*: horse, steed, war-horse

PATER NOSTER, *n.*: paternoster, the Lord's Prayer

PERDEE, *adv.* or *interj.*: indeed

PIN, *n.*: ("And I can make a wondrous pin") peg, nail

PO, *n.*: peacock

Q

QUAINT, *adv.*: ("Why act ye so quaint?") strangely, queerly

R

Resurrex a mortruis! (Latin): "Risen from among the dead." Coll thinks he must have been dead rather than asleep.

S

SEIGNEURS, *n.*: great lords, persons of high rank

SHRIFT, *n.*: *literally*, a confession. In "Yet must I make better shrift," Mak means that he must make up a better story if he is to get away with this theft.

SHROGS, *n.*: thickets

SMART, *adv.*: quickly

SOUTHERN TOOTH, *idiom*: "Now take out that Southern tooth" means "Stop talking with a South of England accent." In other words, "Don't put on airs!"

SIEGE, *n.*: ruling lord or king

SPED, *past pasticiple of v.*: ("But quickly let it be sped") finished

STAY, *v.*: "(Stay thy hand") hold

SWINK, *v.*: toil, labor, work

T

TALE, *n*.: ("No matter what the tale") cost

TENORY, *n*.: tenor, the highest part in a male chorus

TENNIS, *n*.: ("And play withal at the tennis") It may seem odd to us that a shepherd should offer a tennis ball to the Infant Jesus. In those days, the game of tennis had recently been introduced into Europe from the East, and was played only by royalty and the highest nobility. Therefore, Daw's gift is a symbol of Christ's majesty.

THERETILL, *adv*.: thereto

THWANG, *v*.: suffer a whipping

W

WARLOCK, *n*.: wizard, sorcerer, the Devil

WEATHER, *n*.: storm, *bad* weather

WEFT, *n*.: woof, threads used in weaving. "Ill-spun weft, I wiss, ever comes ill out," means, "Badly spun thread, indeed, always makes poor cloth."

WIN, *v*.: ("To the door will I win") go

WITHAL, *conj*.: ("Withal she has a house full of children") although